It's another Quality Book from CGP

This book is for anyone doing Key Stage Three Spanish.

It contains lots of tricky questions designed
to make you sweat — because that's the only
way you'll get any better.

It's also got a couple of daft bits in to try and make the whole
experience at least vaguely entertaining for you.

What CGP is all about

Our sole aim here at CGP is to produce the highest quality
books — carefully written, immaculately presented and
dangerously close to being funny.

Then we work our socks off to get them out to you
— at the cheapest possible prices.

Contents

Published by CGP

Editors:

Heather Gregson
Rachel Grocott
Sabrina Robinson

Contributors:

Janice Crossfield
Deborah McNee
Graham Whittaker

With thanks to Emma Warhurst, Anne Hennessey and Glenda Simpson for the proofreading.

ISBN: 978 1 84762 887 9

Clipart from Corel®
Printed by Elanders Ltd, Newcastle upon Tyne.

Based on the classic CGP style created by Richard Parsons.

Numbers

Q1 Write a number from the circle to match each Spanish word. Be careful, there's one extra number which you need to write out in Spanish yourself.

a) diez ☐   d) siete ☐

b) tres ☐   e) seis ☐

c) dos ☐   f) .... ☐

7 3 2

5 6 10

Q2 Write out the sums in words, in Spanish. I've done the first one for you.

a) 3 + 2 = 5   *tres + dos = cinco* ....   d) 18 + 2 = 20 ....

b) 7 − 1 = 6 ....   e) 14 − 13 = 1 ....

c) 8 + 4 = 12 ....   f) 15 − 2 = 13 ....

Q3 Write out these numbers in words, in Spanish. I've done the first one for you.

a) 91   *noventa y uno* ....   f) 27 ....   k) 73 ....

b) 34 ....   g) 43 ....   l) 61 ....

c) 39 ....   h) 100 ....   m) 99 ....

d) 88 ....   i) 52 ....   n) 86 ....

e) 48 ....   j) 78 ....   o) 65 ....

Q4 Which floor does each of these people live on? Write the answer next to their name.

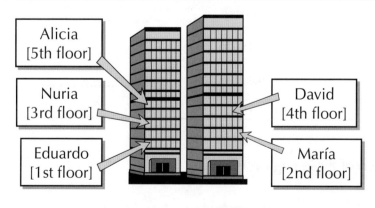

Alicia [5th floor]

Nuria [3rd floor]

Eduardo [1st floor]

David [4th floor]

María [2nd floor]

a) Nuria = ... *tercero* ....

b) María = ...

c) Alicia = ...

d) David = ...

e) Eduardo = ...

Spanish numbers — as easy as Juan, two, three...

Numbers get everywhere — from how many sugars you have in your tea to how many pets you have — you just can't avoid them. So that means that you need to know them off by heart. You'd better get going...

Times and Dates

Q1   Draw hands on the clocks to show the times written beneath.

a) Son las cinco.   b) Son las nueve y media.   c) Es la una menos cuarto.

d) Son las tres menos cinco.   e) Son las cuatro y veinticinco.   f) Son las dos y cinco.

Q2   Write down the times shown on these clocks. The first one has been done for you.

a) ....*Son las tres.*....................   b) ....   c) ....

d) ....   e) ....   f) ....

Q3   Write out these words in English.

a) viernes ....   e) martes ....

b) domingo..................................   f) sábado ....

c) miércoles ....   g) los viernes...............................

d) jueves....................................   h) lunes ....

Q4   Circle the correct translation for each of these English words.

a) tomorrow = *ayer / mañana*   d) yesterday = *hoy / ayer*

b) weekend = *el fin de semana / hoy*   e) week = *la semana / la tarde*

c) afternoon = *la mañana / la tarde*   f) night = *mañana / la noche*

Times and Dates

Q1   Choose a month from the box on the right to go with each of the descriptions.

a) The month of Christmas. ....

b) One of the hottest months of the year. ....

c) Halloween is in this Autumn month. ....

d) The month of Valentine's Day. ....

e) A month in Spring. ....

febrero
abril
agosto
octubre
diciembre

Q2   Circle the correct date for each of these people's birthday.

a) 22/4
el veintidós de abril
OR
el dos de abril

d) 14/7
el siete de mayo
OR
el catorce de julio

b) 6/10
el seis de noviembre
OR
el seis de octubre

e) 6/12
el tres de junio
OR
el seis de diciembre

c) 13/1
el tres de enero
OR
el trece de enero

f) 5/5
el cinco de mayo
OR
el quince de agosto

Q3   Write the following dates in Spanish.

a) 17th September ....

b) 22nd November ....

c) 14th June ....

d) 2nd March ....

e) 21st July ....

f) 1st January ....

Meeting and Greeting

Q1 Write down in Spanish how you would greet someone
at these different times of day (p.s. don't just use 'hola').

These phrases all
start with 'Buenos'
or 'Buenas'.

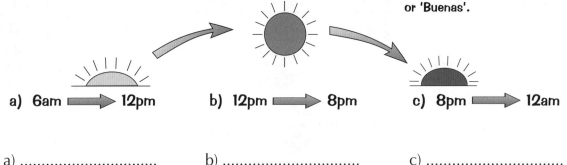

a) 6am ➡ 12pm   **b)** 12pm ➡ 8pm   **c)** 8pm ➡ 12am

a) ....   b) ....   c) ....

Q2 Complete the Spanish for the following words.

Hey, good lookin'...

a) Hello ➡ H....................   b) Goodbye ➡ A....................

c) See you later ➡ H.......... l..........   d) See you soon ➡ H.......... p..........

Q3 Circle the expression that you'd be most likely to use in the following situations:

a) You are about to go upstairs to bed: *Buenos días / Buenas noches*

b) You meet your teacher in town in the afternoon: *Hasta pronto / Buenas tardes*

c) You see your friend at the park: *Hola / Adiós*

d) You ask your brother how he is: *¿Cómo está? / ¿Qué tal?*

e) You say goodbye to your friend who you are going to see again later: *Hasta luego / Hola*

f) You greet your exchange partner's parents at the breakfast table: *Buenas tardes / Buenos días*

Q4 Here is a conversation between a teacher (Señor García) and a pupil (Lucas).
Fill in the missing words in Spanish using the words in brackets to help you.

SEÑOR GARCÍA:	....*[Hello]*, Lucas.
LUCAS:	....*[Good day]*, Señor García.
	....*[How are you?]*
SEÑOR GARCÍA:	....*[Fine, thanks.]* ....*[See you later.]*
LUCAS:	....*[Goodbye]*, Señor García.

Meeting and Greeting

Q1   Circle the answer that describes how these people are feeling. Use the faces to help you.

a)

¿Cómo estás, Ana?

Muy bien / Fatal

c)

¿Qué tal, Sara?

Muy bien / Fatal

b)

¿Y tú, Roberto?

Fatal / Bien

d)

¿Y tú, Carmen?

No muy bien / Bien

Q2   Match the Spanish sentences on the left with the correct English ones on the right.

Encantado.	**Let me introduce my friend.**
Le presento a mi tío.	**This is my friend, Olivia.**
¿Cómo está tu madre?	**Pleased to meet you.**
Estoy muy bien, gracias.	**How is your mother?**
Este es mi hermano.	**Let me introduce my uncle.**
Le presento a mi amigo.	**This is my brother.**
Esta es mi amiga, Olivia.	**I'm very well, thank you.**

Q3   Arturo is introducing Ignacio to Mireia. Use the phrases in the box to help you fill in the speech bubbles.

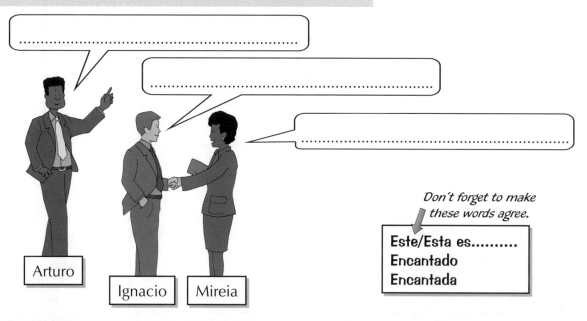

Don't forget to make these words agree.

Este/Esta es..........
Encantado
Encantada

Arturo

Ignacio   Mireia

6

6

Being Polite

Q1 Unscramble the Spanish words on the left and write them out correctly. Then draw lines to match the Spanish word to the English meaning on the right. I've done the first one for you.

a) iasgrca .... *gracias* .... please

b) rop vfaor .... thank you

c) ol iensto .... thank you very much

d) ed anda .... I'm sorry

e) hasmuc raiasgc.................................. you're welcome

You could have just said 'excuse me'...

Q2 Fill in the these words for different ways of saying 'excuse me'.

a) You want to ask someone for directions: P __ r __ o n __

b) You want to attract someone's attention: P __ r f __ __ o r

c) Someone is in the way and you want to get past: C __ __ p __ r m __ s __

Q3 Use the words from above to help you complete these conversations.

a) **SOFÍA**: Pilar, ¿quieres ir a la piscina mañana?

   PILAR: .... *[I'm sorry]*, pero no me gusta nadar.

   SOFÍA: ¿Te gusta la playa?

   PILAR: .... *[I'm really sorry]*. Odio la playa también.

b) **JAIME**: .... *[Excuse me]*, ¿hay un banco por aquí?

   ALBA: Sí. Está al lado del cine.

   JAIME: .... *[Thank you very much]*.

   ALBA: .... *[You're welcome]*.

c) **TERESA**: Buenos días.

   VENDEDORA: ¿Sí, señora?

   TERESA: Tres kilos de plátanos, ... *[please]*.

   VENDEDORA: ¿Algo más?

   TERESA: .... *[No, thank you]*.

I said 'tres', not 'treinta'...

__Being Polite__

Q1 Write the correct name to answer each of the questions below.

Gabriel — Quisiera ir al cine.

David — Quisiera una hamburguesa.

María — Quisiera un bocadillo de queso.

Ana — Quisiera un zumo.

Eva — Quisiera cenar.

Álvaro — Quisiera un café con leche.

a) Who wants a juice? .... d) Who wants to go to the cinema? ....
b) Who wants a coffee with milk? .... e) Who wants a hamburger? ....
c) Who wants to have dinner? .... f) Who wants a cheese sandwich? ....

Q2 You are at your friend's house. Look at the pictures below and use '**¿Puedo...?**' ('May I...?') to ask if you can do these activities. Use the expressions in the box to help you.

| beber leche | escuchar música | ver la televisión |
| poner la mesa | ~~comer galletas~~ | jugar al fútbol |

a) ¿Puedo comer galletas?

b) ....

c) ....

d) ....

e) ....

f) ....

Your Details

Q1 Write a sentence in Spanish to answer each of these questions about yourself.

a) ¿Cuántos años tienes? ....

b) ¿Cómo te llamas? ....

c) ¿Cuándo es tu cumpleaños? ....

d) ¿Qué te gusta hacer? ....

Q2 Choose the most suitable adjective from the box to complete each description of someone's personality. Make sure each adjective has the correct ending.

| deportista | perezoso/a | ~~trabajador(a)~~ | simpático/a | tímido/a |

a) Me llamo Víctor. Trabajo mucho. Soy ....*trabajador.*...............

b) Me llamo Roberto. Me gusta el fútbol. Soy ....

c) Me llamo Rosa. Tengo muchas amigas. Soy ....

d) Me llamo Ángela. Me gusta dormir. Soy ....

e) Me llamo Alberto. No me gusta hablar. Soy ....

Q3 Write sentences in Spanish describing yourself as if you were each of these people. I've done the first one for you.

> Make sure you use a verb and try to link some of the details with "y" (and).

> Soy bajo. Llevo gafas.

a) Michael — tall, green eyes, short hair.

   Me llamo Michael. Soy alto. Tengo los ojos verdes y el pelo corto.

b) Jasmine — short, brown eyes, blonde hair.

   ....

c) David — blue eyes, black hair, wears glasses.

   ....

d) Sophie — medium height, slim, long hair.

   ....

e) Gareth — fat, red hair, doesn't wear glasses.

   ....

Your Family

Q1 Write down the Spanish for each of these family members.

a) my mother   b) my grandfather   c) my uncle   d) my sister

....

e) my father   f) my grandmother   g) my brother   h) my aunt

....

Q2 Read Marina's email and fill in the missing information in the table in English.

> Me llamo Marina y tengo catorce años.
>
> Mi madre se llama Jenny y tiene treinta y cinco años. Mi padrastro se llama Peter y tiene cuarenta años. Mi hermanastra se llama Megan y tiene dos años más que yo. Mi hermano se llama Joe y tiene once años.
>
> Mi mejor amiga se llama Louise y ella tiene catorce años también.

Ugh, siblings...

Name	Age	Relationship
....	35	mother
Peter	....	....
....	16	stepsister
Joe	11	....
Louise	....	best friend

Q3 Write out these sentences in Spanish.

a) I have two brothers and a sister.

....

b) I'm called Rebecca. I am an only child.

....

c) My sister is called Emma and she is ten years old.

....

d) My cousin is called Matthew and he is nice.

....

Pets and Animals

Q1   Write down the English for these animals.

    a) un perro   b)   un caballo   c) un pájaro

    ....

Q2   Write down either '**un**' or '**una**' and the Spanish word for each of these animals.

English	un / una	Spanish
cat	....	....
mouse	....	....
tortoise	....	....
hamster	....	....
rabbit	....	....

Q3   Read what these people say about their pets, then answer the questions below.

No tengo animales en casa. — **Nerea**

Tengo un caballo blanco. Se llama Alba. — **Marta**

Tengo dos gatos negros. — **Esteban**

Mi perro es muy gordo. — **Emiliano**

Tengo un conejo gris. Se llama Ramito y es muy bonito. — **Ana**

    a) What does Esteban say about his pets? ....

    b) Who has no pets? ....

    c) What kind of animal is Alba? ....

    d) What three things does Ana say about her rabbit?

        ....

    e) Who has a very fat dog? ....

Q4   In Spanish, write a sentence about your pet. If you don't have any pets, write that in Spanish.

    ....

My younger brother's a little monkey — does he count as a pet?
This page isn't so bad — everyone loves animals, right? Sadly, you can't just learn the animal names though — you need to be able to recognise the question "¿Tienes animales en casa?" and answer it, too.

Your Home

Q1   Talk about a typo — these Spanish words for rooms in a house have all been misspelt. Unscramble the letters and write the correct name of each room in Spanish.

a) le urtoca ed oñba   ....   d) le oriomordit   ....

b) al incaco   ....   e) le andríj   ....

c) le rocomed   ....   f) le lasnó   ....

Q2   Write down the Spanish for these items of furniture. Don't forget 'un' or 'una'.

a) a table   b) a bed   c) a wardrobe

....

d) a sofa   e) a chair   f) an armchair

....

Q3   Read Manuel's description of his house, then answer the questions in English.

> En mi casa hay seis habitaciones. Hay un salón bastante grande, una cocina y un cuarto de baño. Hay tres dormitorios. Mi dormitorio es pequeño pero me gusta mucho. Hay una cama, una mesa y un armario. También hay un jardín muy bonito.

a) How many rooms are there in Manuel's house? ....

b) How does he describe the living room? ....

c) How many bedrooms are there? ....

d) What furniture is there in Manuel's bedroom? ....

Q4   In full sentences, answer these questions about your house and bedroom in Spanish.

a) ¿Qué habitaciones hay en tu casa?

....

....

b) ¿Qué muebles hay en tu dormitorio?

....

....

Where You Live

Q1 Write down the Spanish for the following words.

    a) a flat   b) a house   c) a village   d) a city

....

Q2 How do you ask a friend where they live in Spanish?

....

Q3 Write out in Spanish what each person is saying about where they live.

I live in the north-west of Spain. (Inés)

I live near the sea. (Carlos)

I live in the east of Spain. (Patricia)

I live in the south of Spain. (Sergio)

Inés: ....

Carlos: ....

Patricia: ....

Sergio: ....

Q4 Read what these people think about where they live. Write 'P' for a positive opinion, 'N' for a negative opinion and 'P/N' for a positive and a negative opinion.

"Vivo en las montañas. No me gusta porque es aburrido." — **Adriana** [ ]

"Vivo en un pueblo en el norte. Es tranquilo pero es sucio." — **Ana** [ ]

"Vivo en Granada, en el sur. Es preciosa y muy divertida." — **Orlando** [ ]

"Vivo cerca del mar. Me gusta la ciudad porque es muy bonita." — **María** [ ]

"Vivo en Málaga. Me encanta vivir aquí porque es estupendo." — **Jorge** [ ]

"Vivo en un pueblo en el campo. Es limpio pero es aburrido." — **Antonia** [ ]

Daily Routine

Q1 Complete the sentences about daily routine, choosing from the phrases in the box. Then match them up to their English meanings.

a) Vuelvo ....*a casa.*........   I watch TV.

b) Hago ....   I go to school.

c) Veo ....   I do my homework.

d) Me lavo ....   I brush my teeth.

e) Voy ....   I come back home.

> *mis deberes.*   *los dientes.*   *a casa.*   *al instituto.*   *la televisión.*

Q2 Write out these sentences in Spanish.

a) I have dinner. ....

b) I get up. ....

c) I get dressed. ....

d) I have breakfast. ....

e) I wake up. ....

f) I go to bed. ....

Q3 For each picture, write a sentence to describe your daily routine, plus the time you do each thing. The first one has been done for you.

a) *Me lavo a las siete y media.* — 7.30am

b) .... — 7.45am

c) .... — 8.15am

d) .... — 4.20pm

e) .... — 6pm

f) .... — 9.30pm

How do you say "I lie in until midday"?

Daily routine is an __easy one to practise__ the day before a test. When you leave school say, "__Vuelvo a casa__". When you sit down to eat your dinner, say "__Ceno__" and so on. Who cares if people look at you funny...

<u>Chores</u>

Q1   Choose a verb from the box to complete these sentences.

a) .... los platos.

b) .... la aspiradora.

c) .... mi dormitorio.

d) .... mi cama.

e) .... la mesa.

> Lavo   Paso
>   Arreglo
> Hago   Pongo

Q2   Write down what these sentences mean in English.

a) Hago la compra. ....

b) Lavo el coche. ....

c) No hago nada. ....

d) Limpio la casa. ....

Q3   How do you ask a friend if they help at home in Spanish?

....

Q4   Write out in Spanish what these people say about their chores.
The first one has already been done for you.

> The things I'll do for pocket money...

a) **Jake**: On Sundays I wash the car.

Los domingos lavo el coche.

b) **Sarah**: On Mondays I make my bed and I tidy my bedroom.

....

c) **Richard**: On Tuesdays I do the vacuuming and I do the shopping.

....

d) **Louise**: I lay the table and I wash the dishes.

....

e) **Paul**: I don't do anything. I am very lazy.

....

The Body

Q1   Here are two lists of words for parts of the body. Draw lines to match up the Spanish on the left with the English on the right.

el dedo	tooth
la mano	eye
el pelo	finger
el ojo	mouth
el diente	hair
la boca	hand

Q2   Some joker has taken the vowels out of my keyboard. Fill in the missing letters of these body parts and then say what they mean in English. I've done the first one for you.

a) l _a_ g _a_ r g _a_ n t _a_ = ... *throat* ....

b) l __ __ s p __ l d __ = ...

c) __ l b r __ z __ = ...

d) l __ r __ d __ l l __ = ...

e) __ l c __ __ __ l l __ = ...

f) l __ n __ r __ z = ...

g) l __ __ r __ j __ = ...

Q3   Write the Spanish for these words:

a) (the head) ....   b) (the body) ....

Q4   Label the body parts marked on the diagram in Spanish.

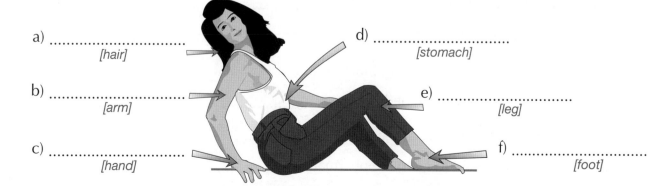

a) .... [hair]   d) .... [stomach]

b) .... [arm]   e) .... [leg]

c) .... [hand]   f) .... [foot]

Health and Illness

Q1 Write down the Spanish for these items that you might buy from the pharmacy.

a) some tablets

....

b) a plaster

....

c) a cream

....

d) a syrup

....

Q2 Complete each sentence correctly by writing '**me duele**' or '**me duelen**'.

a) .... la garganta.

b) .... los ojos.

c) .... los oídos.

d) .... el estómago.

e) .... la cabeza.

f) .... los pies.

Q3 These Spanish students are visiting the UK, but they're all complaining that they're ill. Read what each of them says is wrong, then answer the questions below.

Estoy enfermo. Me duele el cuello y me duele la cabeza. Quiero unas pastillas.

Me duele la espalda. Voy a la cama porque me duelen las piernas y los pies.

Me duele la garganta. Necesito un jarabe. Quiero ir a la farmacia.

Iván

Tengo gripe. Me duelen la cabeza y la garganta. Quiero ir al médico.

Javier

Ay, me duelen los dedos. Quiero ir a la farmacia para comprar una crema.

Paula

José

Lucía

a) Which two people have headaches? ....

b) What's wrong with Paula? ....

c) What does Paula say she needs? ....

d) Who has flu? ....

e) Why does Javier want to go to bed? ....

f) Who wants some cream? ....

g) Which two people want to go to the pharmacy? ....

Section 2 — You, Family and Home

School Subjects

Q1 Write the names of these subjects in Spanish. Include 'el', 'la', 'los' or 'las'.

a)

....

b)

....

c)

....

d)

Hola, me llamo Juan.

Hola, ¿qué tal?

....

e)

....

f)

....

g)

....

h)

....

Q2 Write down the Spanish names for these subjects.

a) history

....

b) physics

....

c) German

....

d) biology

....

e) PE

....

f) religious studies

....

g) French

....

h) science

....

Q3 Read what Jorge has written about his school subjects, then answer the questions on the right with 'T' for true and 'F' for false.

Me llamo Jorge. Estudio ocho asignaturas. Me gusta mucho el inglés porque es fácil y útil. No me gustan las matemáticas porque son difíciles y aburridas. Mi asignatura preferida es la informática porque es muy interesante.

a) He studies eight subjects. ☐

b) He says that English is boring. ☐

c) He likes maths because it's useful. ☐

d) His favourite subject is PE. ☐

e) He thinks IT is very interesting. ☐

Q4 Write two sentences in Spanish about which subjects you like and dislike. *Use Jorge's example above to help you.*

....

....

School Routine

Q1   Look at the pictures and describe how each person gets
      to school in Spanish. The first one has been done for you.

a)    *Voy al instituto en coche.*   b)   ....

c)    ....   d)   ....

Q2   Read about Iván's typical school day then answer the following questions in English.

> Hola, me llamo Iván. Me levanto a las siete y media. Voy al instituto
> en coche. Las clases empiezan a las nueve menos cuarto. Tenemos
> cinco clases por día. Las clases duran una hora. Las clases terminan
> a las tres y media. Cada día hacemos dos horas de deberes.

a) How does Iván get to school? ....

b) What time do his lessons start? ....

c) How many lessons does he have per day? ....

d) How long does each lesson last? ....

e) What happens at 3.30pm? ....

f) What does he say about his homework? ....

Q3   Fill in the gaps by adding a present tense verb in Spanish.   *Use Iván's example
                                                                      above to help you.*

a) .... *[I get up]* a las ocho.

b) Las clases .... *[start]* a las nueve.

c) Las clases .... *[end]* a las cuatro y media.

d) .... *[We have]* ocho clases por día.

e) .... *[We do]* una hora de deberes por día.

"My dog ate my homework" never works — let that be a lesson to you...
Just when you thought that you couldn't get asked any more school questions, here are two whole pages
of them. Sigh. Teachers love them though, so make sure you know how to talk about your school routine.

Classroom Stuff

Q1   How do you say the following school words in Spanish?

Remember to write 'un'
or 'una' for each word.

pupil

a) ....

b) ....

c) ....

d) ....

e) ....

Q2   These commands are all things you might hear in the classroom.
Circle the correct English translation for each one.

a) ¡Levántate!
Stop it! / Stand up!

b) ¡Silencio!
Silence! / Get out!

c) ¡Siéntate!
Sit down! / Silence!

Q3   Write out how you would say these in English.

a) Falso ....

b) Verdadero ....

c) ¿Qué quiere decir eso? ....

d) ¿Cómo se dice en inglés? ....

e) ¿Cómo se dice en español? ....

Q4   Decide if the following classroom objects are masculine or feminine. Write '**un**' for masculine
words and '**una**' for feminine words, then write the word in English. The first one's been done.

a) ....*un*...... libro ➡ ....*a book*.........

b) .... profesora ➡ ....

c) .... cuaderno ➡ ....

d) .... horario ➡ ....

e) .... clase ➡ ....

This is Spain, or
'land of the rabbits',
as I like to call it...

"¡Levántate!" "¡Siéntate!" — it's like musical bumps in our classroom...
Knowing all of your <u>classroom stuff in Spanish</u> will definitely earn you <u>brownie points</u> from your teacher.
You'll get <u>double brownie points</u> too if you can ask how to say something in Spanish, so <u>get practising</u>.

Jobs

Q1   Write a number in each box to match the Spanish jobs with their English translations.

a) el secretario   **4**

b) el policía   ☐

c) el mecánico   ☐

d) el ingeniero   ☐

e) la enfermera   ☐

f) la vendedora   ☐

g) el albañil   ☐

1) mechanic
2) builder
3) nurse
4) ~~secretary~~
5) engineer
6) saleswoman
7) police officer

Q2   Decide if the following Spanish words for jobs are for men, women or both men and women. Write each word under the correct picture.

actriz   ~~enfermero~~   vendedora   enfermera   dentista
albañil   profesor   peluquero   policía

enfermero	....	....
....	....	....
....	....	....

Q3   Write a sentence for each person's job using the pictures below. The first one is done for you.

a) Ana   _Ana es profesora._

b) Pablo   ....

c) Carolina   ....

d) Blanca   ....

e) Carlos   ....

f) Juan   ....

Talking About Jobs

Q1a) You receive a letter from your Spanish friend, telling you about the jobs people do in his family. Some of the words are missing. Read the letter and fill in the missing words from the box.

| semana | restaurante | hospital | hermano | química | divertido |

¡Hola!

Tengo un trabajo a tiempo parcial como camarero en un .... Trabajo los fines de .... y los lunes y martes. Mi ...., Nick, es estudiante. Estudia biología y .... Mi padre es profesor y mi madre es enfermera en un .... En el futuro quiero ser actor porque es ....

Hasta luego, David

b) Now decide if these statements about David's letter are true (T) or false (F).

i)   David works full-time. ☐   iv) Nick studies art. ☐

ii) David works on Wednesdays. ☐   v) David's mother is a nurse. ☐

iii) Nick is a student. ☐   vi) David wants to be a doctor. ☐

Q2 The words in these sentences have been mixed up. Rearrange the words so that the sentences make sense. Use the English translation to help you.

a) ser   médico   quiero   porque   útil   es
[I want to be a doctor because it's useful]

....

b) dentista   quiero   es   porque   interesante   ser
[I want to be a dentist because it's interesting]

....

c) estudiar   porque   inglés   quiero   fácil   es
[I want to study English because it's easy]

....

d) ganan   ingeniero   quiero   ser   mucho   porque   dinero
[I want to be an engineer because they earn a lot of money]

....

e) estudiar   quiero   dibujo   divertido   es   porque
[I want to study art because it's fun]

....

Directions

Q1 Draw lines to match the Spanish questions with the English meaning.
Watch out — you need to write one of the questions in Spanish yourself.

¿Dónde está el teatro?   How do I get to the market?

¿Para ir al mercado?   Where's the cinema?

¿Para ir a la iglesia?   Where's the theatre?

....   How do I get to the church?

Q2 Complete these Spanish directions using the words from the box.

tome	segunda	gire	recto	primera	siga	derecha

a) Go straight ahead. → .... todo ....

b) Turn right. → Gire a la ....

c) Take the second road on the left. → .... la .... calle a la izquierda.

d) Take the first road on the right. → Tome la .... calle a la derecha.

e) Turn left. → .... a la izquierda.

Q3 Look at the map and follow the directions below. Start from X
each time. For each direction, write where you arrive in English.

a) Tome la segunda calle a la derecha.   *railway station* ....

b) Gire a la izquierda.   ....

c) Siga todo recto.   ....

d) Tome la segunda calle a la izquierda. ....

e) Gire a la derecha.   ....

MAP

Q4 Read this conversation then write 'T' for true or 'F' for false in the box next to each statement.

— ¿El castillo está lejos de aquí?
— Sí, está lejos. Está a cinco kilómetros.
— ¿Y el teatro está lejos de aquí?
— No, está cerca. Está a un kilómetro.

a) The castle is far away. ☐

b) The castle is 3km away. ☐

c) The theatre is far away ☐

d) The theatre is 1km away. ☐

Shops

Q1 Fill in the missing Spanish and English words for these shops.
Remember to write '**el**' or '**la**' for each word too.

English	el / la	Spanish
supermarket	....	....
....	....	tienda de comestibles
butcher's	....	....
....	....	confitería
newsagent's	....	....
....	....	panadería

Q2 Draw lines to match these Spanish words for shops with the English meaning.

Caaaam and get ya goldfish — two for a fivah. Lovely wiv ketchup.

la farmacia   *bank*

el banco   *cake shop*

el mercado   *pharmacy*

la biblioteca   *library*

la pastelería   *market*

Q3 Where would you go to do the following things?
Write a Spanish shop from the box for each one.

la pastelería	la farmacia	la carnicería
la tienda de comestibles	la librería	el banco

a) Buy some tomatoes for a salad. ....

b) Change some pounds into euros. ....

c) Buy some cream for your insect bites. ....

d) Buy some meat for your barbecue. ....

e) Buy a Spanish to English dictionary. ....

f) Buy a cream cake. ....

I'm doing online delivery next time...

Don't confuse 'tienda de comestibles' with 'tienda de combustibles'...

If you're planning on <u>going to Spain</u>, this page will help you <u>loads</u> — just <u>imagine</u> if you <u>didn't know</u> where
the <u>cake shop</u> was... Having said that, they'll all come in <u>useful in class</u> too so make sure you <u>practise</u> them.

Places in Town

Q1   Translate this tourist information leaflet into Spanish. The first line has been done for you.

For tourists, there is:

a) a theatre

b) a park

c) a church

d) a museum

e) a town hall

f) a castle

Para los turistas, hay:

a) ......*un teatro*......

b) ....

c) ....

d) ....

e) ....

f) ....

> Look at this, dear — a potato museum!
>
> Ugh.

Q2   Read what these people say about their town, then write the correct name for the questions below. There may be more than one correct name for each question.

Bárbara	*No hay mucho en mi ciudad. Hay un hospital, un ayuntamiento, un parque y una oficina de turismo. ¡No me gusta mi ciudad porque no hay cine!*

Pablo	*En mi ciudad hay un hotel, una iglesia, un parque y Correos. Hay una biblioteca y una librería, pero no hay oficina de turismo.*

Ángela	*Hay mucho que hacer en mi ciudad. Hay un polideportivo, una piscina y un teatro. Hay una estación también, pero no hay hotel para los turistas.*

Who lives in a place which has:

a) a hospital? ....

b) a park? ....

c) a post office? ....

d) a library? ....

e) a station? ....

f) a leisure centre? ....

Q3   Write these sentences about places in town in Spanish.

a) In my town, there is a castle. ....

b) There's no swimming pool. ....

c) There is a museum and a park. ....

d) There's a town hall and a church. ....

e) There's no station in my town. ....

Section 4 — Town, Shopping, Food and Drink

Food and Drink

Q1 Draw lines to match the pictures with the Spanish words. I've done the first one for you.

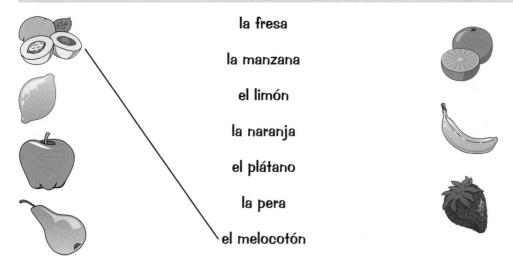

la fresa

la manzana

el limón

la naranja

el plátano

la pera

el melocotón

Q2 Write the Spanish words for these vegetables. Include '**el**', '**la**', '**los**' and '**las**'.

a) potato   ....

b) carrot   ....

c) cauliflower   ....

d) tomato   ....

e) peas   ....

f) beans   ....

g) mushroom   ....

h) onion   ....

Q3 Write in Spanish what these people would like to eat. I've done the first one for you.

a) **beef**
la carne de vaca
....

e) **lamb**
....

b) **pork**
....

f) **ham**
....

c) **chicken**
....

g) **fish**
....

d) **seafood**
....

h) **sausage**
....

Food and Drink

Q1   Draw lines to match the pictures with the Spanish words.

el chocolate

la galleta

el pastel

la mermelada

el azúcar

el helado

Q2   The vowels have been removed from these dairy products. Fill in the missing vowels in the Spanish words then write out their English translation. The first one's been done for you.

a) l <u>a</u> m <u>a</u> n t <u>e</u> q u <u>i</u> l l <u>a</u> = ...<i>butter</i>............   d) l _   n _ t _   = ...

b) _ l   y _ g _ r   = ...   e) _ l   h _ _ v _ = ...

c) l _   l _ c h _   = ...   f) _ l   q _ _ s _ = ...

Q3   Translate the Spanish drinks list into English. The first one's already been done.

CAFÉ ALBA
a) café con leche
b) café
c) té
d) chocolate caliente
e) limonada
f) zumo de naranja
g) agua mineral
h) vino tinto
i) vino blanco
j) cerveza

a)   ....<i>coffee with milk</i>........   f)   ....

b)   ....   g)   ....

c)   ....   h)   ....

d)   ....   i)   ....

e)   ....   j)   ....

Q4   Write these words for foods in Spanish. Include 'el', 'la', 'los' or 'las'.

a) cereal   ....   e) sandwich   ....

b) chips   ....   f) bread   ....

c) rice   ....   g) pasta   ....

d) soup   ....   h) hamburger   ....

Food and Drink

Q1   Read Esteban's email and then make a list of the foods he likes and doesn't like in English.

SEND   To: julia@myemailbox.net
        Subject: La comida

Hola Julia,
¿Qué tal? Voy a hablar de mi comida preferida. Me gusta el helado y el chocolate. Me gustan las fresas, las peras y los plátanos. No me gusta la lechuga y no me gusta la coliflor. No me gustan los guisantes porque son horribles y no me gusta el filete porque soy vegetariano.
Hasta pronto, Esteban.

✓ Esteban likes...	✗ Esteban doesn't like...
....	....
....	....
....	....
....	....
....	....

Q2   Complete the translation of these conversations in Spanish.

TOM: Ben, are you thirsty?
BEN: No, I'm not thirsty.

→

TOM: Ben, _¿tienes sed?_ ....
BEN: No, ...

ABI: Meg, are you hungry?
MEG: Yes, I'm hungry.

→

ABI: Meg, ...
MEG: Sí, ...

Q3   Write these sentences about mealtimes in Spanish. The first one has been done for you.

a) .... _Desayuno a las ocho._ .... [I have breakfast at 8 o'clock.]

b) .... [I eat cereal and drink coffee.]

c) .... [I have lunch at half past 12.]

d) .... [I eat a ham sandwich.]

e) .... [I have dinner at quarter past 7.]

f) .... [I eat chicken, rice and carrots.]

Food and Drink

Q1   Write the Spanish word from the box to match these clues. I've done the first one for you.

> el postre   la carta   el plato principal   la cuenta
>   el restaurante   la camarera   el primer plato   ~~el camarero~~

a) The person who serves you = ... *el camarero* ....*[male]*

.................................*[female]*

b) The list of dishes you can choose from = ...

c) The small dish eaten at the start of a meal = ...

d) The piece of paper which tells you how much to pay = ...

e) Something sweet eaten at the end of a meal = ...

f) The place where you go to have a meal = ...

g) The biggest course of the meal = ...

Q2   You're at a Spanish restaurant. Use the menu to help you fill in your parts of this conversation in Spanish. The bits in brackets tell you what to say.

Camarero: Buenas tardes.

a) **You:**   ....
    [A table for one please.]

Camarero: ¿Qué quiere de primer plato?

b) **You:**   ....
    [I'd like the salad please.]

Camarero: ¿Qué quiere de plato principal?

c) **You:**   ....
    [I'd like the fish with rice.]

Camarero: ¿Qué quiere de postre?

d) **You:**   ....
    [I'd like the chocolate cake.]

Camarero: ¿Y para beber?

e) **You:**   ....
    [I'd like a mineral water.]

    And when you've finished your meal...

f) **You:**   ....
    [The bill, please.]

> Restaurante
> de Pedro
>
> **PRIMER PLATO**
> Sopa de tomate
> Ensalada
>
> **PLATO PRINCIPAL**
> Salchichas con patatas
> Pescado con arroz
> Pasta con champiñones
>
> **POSTRE**
> Helado de fresa
> Pastel de chocolate
> Fruta (manzana o pera)
>
> **BEBIDAS**
> Zumo de fruta
> Vino
> Agua mineral

Clothes and Colours

Q1   Write the Spanish for these clothes. Include 'el', 'la', 'los' and 'las'.

a) trousers ....   f) hat ....

b) jumper ....   g) dress ....

c) shirt ....   h) jacket ....

d) socks ....   i) T-shirt ....

e) skirt ....   j) shoes ....

Q2   David has sent you a photo of himself and his friends. To help you work out who's who, he's described what everyone is wearing. Read his description and answer the questions.

> Yo, David, llevo pantalones, una camisa y un jersey. Miguel lleva pantalones y una camiseta. Ana lleva una falda y una camiseta. Antonio lleva pantalones y una chaqueta. Julia lleva un vestido.

a) Who is wearing a jacket? ....

b) Who is wearing a jumper? ....

c) What is Ana wearing? ....

d) What is Julia wearing? ....

Q3   Two friends are going to a themed birthday party where they have to wear as many different colours as possible. Complete the descriptions of their outfits.

Remember to make sure all the adjectives agree correctly.

Nadia

Llevo una falda ....[green], un ....[jumper] naranja, un sombrero ....[blue], unos zapatos ....[red] y unos calcetines ....[yellow].

José

Llevo unos ....[trousers] rojos, una camisa ....[pink], una corbata ....[white], una ....[jacket] marrón, unos.........................[socks] negros y unos zapatos ....[grey].

Q4   Describe your school uniform or an imaginary one that you would like to wear. Don't forget to say what colour each item is and to make the colours agree.

Use Nadia and José's examples to help you.

....
....
....

Clothes and Colours

Q1 Draw lines to match the Spanish phrases with their English meaning. I've done the first one for you.

What?! I literally had NOTHING to wear...

¿Algo más?   I would like a skirt.

¿Tiene calcetines?   Is that all?

¿En qué puedo servirle?   How much is it?

¿Es todo?   Do you have any socks?

¿Cuánto cuesta?   Anything else?

Quisiera una falda.   How can I help you?

Q2 Look at the list of clothes in this shop's sale and then fill in the missing questions and answers in Spanish. I've done the first one for you.

Don't forget to use 'cuesta' for clothes that are singular and 'cuestan' for ones that are plural.

a) ¿Cuánto cuesta una camiseta?   *Cuesta siete euros.*
....

b) ¿Cuánto cuestan unos zapatos? ....

c) ¿Cuánto cuesta una falda?   ....

d) ¿Cuánto cuesta un vestido?   ....

e) .... Cuestan veinte euros.

f) .... Cuesta ocho euros.

g) .... Cuestan cinco euros.

✄REBAJAS✄

pantalones 20€
falda 18€
sombrero 8€
zapatos 25€
vestido 23€
calcetines 5€
camiseta 7€

Q3 You're in a Spanish shop buying clothes. Write in the missing parts of the conversation in Spanish. The bits in brackets tell you what to say.

Vendedora: ¿En qué puedo servirle?

a) .... *[Say you'd like a blue hat.]*

Vendedora: Sí, aquí tiene.

b) .... *[Ask how much it costs.]*

Vendedora: Cinco euros.

c) .... *[Say you'll buy it.]*

Tengo una camisa negra — y roja y azul y verde...

Whether you're a <u>shopaholic</u> or not, knowing how to have a <u>conversation in a clothes shop</u> is pretty <u>useful</u>. And as my <u>Grandad</u> says, you don't want to be <u>ripped off</u> and <u>pay a fortune</u> for a pair of <u>jeans full of holes</u>...

Sports and Musical Instruments

Q1 Fill in the gaps to complete these words for sports in Spanish.

a) El _ ú _ _ o _

b) El _ e _ i _

c) El _ a _ o _ _ e _ _ o

d) El _ o _ _ e _

e) El a _ e _ _ e _

f) El _ i _ _ - _ o _ _

Q2 Carlos has made a list of which musical instruments his friends play.
Read his notes and answer the questions below in English.

Miguel: el clarinete y el piano

Flora: la flauta y el clarinete

Alejandro: la batería y el violín

Julia: la trompeta y la guitarra

Enrique: el violín y el piano

Juan: el violoncelo y la flauta

Nora: la trompeta y el piano

Begoña: la batería y la guitarra

a) How many people play the piano? ....

b) How many people play the drums? ....

c) Which instrument is only played by one person?

....

d) What does Flora play?

....

e) What does Julia play?

....

Q3 Complete each of these sentences using either '**toco**' or '**juego**'.

a) .... al baloncesto con mis amigos.

b) .... la flauta en la orquesta de mi instituto.

c) .... la guitarra todos los días.

d) .... al ajedrez con mi padre.

e) .... al tenis porque es divertido.

> Bring it on, kid.
> I was playing tennis when
> you were in nappies.

Q4 Write these sentences in Spanish.

a) I play the cello.

....

b) I play basketball.

....

c) I play rugby.

....

d) I play the drums.

....

Pastimes and Hobbies

Q1 My computer has gone barmy and jumbled up all the letters in these words. Unscramble them and write out each sentence about hobbies in Spanish.

a) ovy a radna

....

b) ohag dossiermen

....

c) ahgo gofinot

....

d) hoag cariobe

....

e) yov ed spramco

....

f) goah miccosil

....

Q2 Read these opinions about different pastimes, then answer the questions below in English.

Person	Opinion
Alfredo	No me gusta ir a nadar porque es cansado.
Vanessa	Me gusta mucho ir de compras porque es divertido.
Osvaldo	Me gusta hacer senderismo porque es interesante.
Raimundo	Me encanta hacer esquí. ¡Es fácil!
Emelina	Hago footing pero no me gusta. Es aburrido.

a) Which hobby does Osvaldo find interesting? ....

b) What does Vanessa think of going shopping? ....

c) Why does Alfredo not like swimming? ....

d) Why does Raimundo like to go skiing? ....

e) Which hobby does Emelina find boring? ....

Q3 Complete these sentences by writing the words in brackets in Spanish.

a) Me gusta hacer ....[cycling] porque es ....[easy].

b) No me gusta hacer ....[hiking] porque es ....[boring].

c) Me encanta hacer ....[aerobics] porque es ....[fun].

d) Odio hacer ....[jogging] porque es ....[difficult]

TV, Books and Radío

Q1 Draw a line to connect each Spanish sentence to the correct English meaning.

Veo la televisión

Leo revistas

Escucho música

Leo periódicos

Veo películas

Leo libros

Escucho la radio

I read books

I listen to music

I listen to the radio

I watch films

I read newspapers

I watch TV

I read magazines

Q2 Read what these three people say then answer the questions below in English.

No escucho música y no me gusta escuchar la radio. Me gusta leer. Me encanta leer libros y revistas.

Lisa

Me gusta ver la televisión y me encanta ver películas. Leo revistas pero odio leer periódicos. Son aburridos.

Venus

Me encanta escuchar música y me gusta ver películas. No leo libros pero me gusta leer revistas y periódicos.

Vincent

a) Which person likes watching TV? ....

b) Which person does not like listening to the radio? ....

c) What do all three people like to read? ....

d) Which person likes to listen to music? ....

e) Which two people like to watch films? ....

f) What does Venus hate to read? ....

g) Which person loves to read books? ....

Q3 Write in Spanish how you would say:

a) I like this film. ....

b) I don't like this film. ....

c) I like this book. ....

d) I don't like this book. ....

Going Out and Making Arrangements

Q1 Where would you go if you wanted to do the following things?
Write the correct Spanish word from the box.

a) to have a good meal .... *el restaurante* ....

b) to go swimming ....

c) to watch a play ....

d) to walk the dog ....

e) to see a film ....

f) to play indoor sports ....

g) to go to bed ....

el centro	la piscina
mi casa	el teatro
el restaurante	el parque
el polideportivo	el cine

Q2 These people all want to go to different places. Write out what their suggestions would be in Spanish. The first one has been done for you.

a)   b)   c)   d)   e)   f)

a) .... *Vamos al centro.* ....   d) ....

b) ....   e) ....

c) ....   f) ....

Q3 Read this conversation then write whether each statement is true (T) or false (F).

Vito:	Hola Mariluz. ¡Vamos a la piscina!
Mariluz:	No gracias, Vito. No me gusta nadar.
Vito:	Vamos al cine. Hay una película de Johnny Depp.
Mariluz:	Me encanta el cine pero no tengo dinero. Lo siento.
Vito:	¡Vamos al parque!
Mariluz:	¡Sí, buena idea! El parque es muy bonito.

a) Vito's first suggestion is to go to the beach. ☐

b) Mariluz says she doesn't like swimming. ☐

c) Vito's second suggestion is to go to the theatre. ☐

d) Mariluz hates the cinema. ☐

e) Mariluz says she has no money. ☐

f) Vito's third suggestion is to go to the park. ☐

g) Mariluz says the park is boring. ☐

Going Out and Making Arrangements

Q1   Read the following arrangements for going out and fill in the grid below in English.

Nos encontramos en el centro a las once menos cuarto.

Rubén

Nos encontramos en el teatro a las ocho y media.

Yolanda

Nos encontramos delante de la piscina a las diez y cuarto.

Carmen

Nos encontramos delante del cine a las nueve.

Patricio

Nos encontramos en mi casa a las tres.

Iker

Person	Meeting Place	Time
Rubén	*in the town centre*	*10.45*
Carmen	....	....
Iker	....	....
Yolanda	....	....
Patricio	....	....

Q2   Write this conversation in English.

Sorry Frank, I can't make it. I er, need to wash my dog.

Renato: Hola, Marta. Vamos al centro.

....

Marta: Estupendo. ¿Dónde nos encontramos y cuándo nos encontramos?

....

Renato: Nos encontramos delante del teatro a las doce.

....

Q3   Unscramble the words for this Spanish conversation using the English translation to help you. Beware! On each line there is one word that you won't need.

a) ¿cuánto una sello entrada cuesta? *[How much does a ticket cost?]*

....

b) cuesta euros seis pago. *[It costs six euros.]*

....

c) personas por dos quisiera entradas favor. *[I would like two tickets please.]*

....

Transport

Q1 Fill in the gaps in the transport page in Manolo's vocabulary book.

Spanish	English		Spanish	English
a) el autobús	....		e)	car
b)	coach		f) el metro	....
c) el avión	....		g)	motorbike
d)	boat		h) la bicicleta	....

Q2 Read what these people say and answer the questions in English.

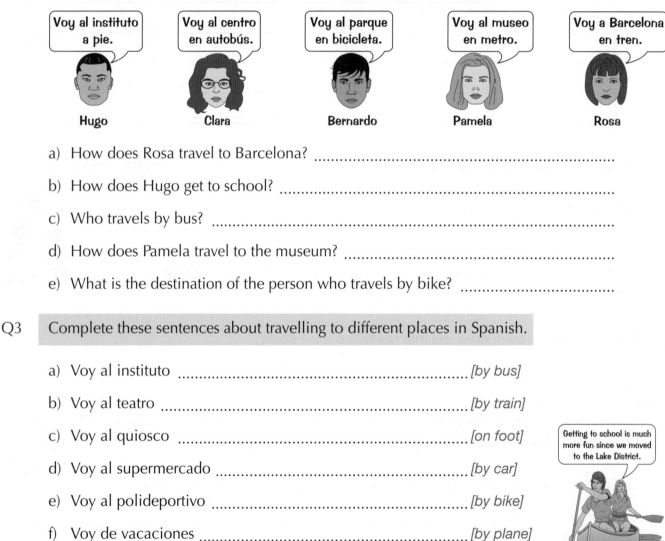

Voy al instituto a pie. — Hugo

Voy al centro en autobús. — Clara

Voy al parque en bicicleta. — Bernardo

Voy al museo en metro. — Pamela

Voy a Barcelona en tren. — Rosa

a) How does Rosa travel to Barcelona? ....

b) How does Hugo get to school? ....

c) Who travels by bus? ....

d) How does Pamela travel to the museum? ....

e) What is the destination of the person who travels by bike? ....

Q3 Complete these sentences about travelling to different places in Spanish.

a) Voy al instituto .... [by bus]

b) Voy al teatro .... [by train]

c) Voy al quiosco .... [on foot]

d) Voy al supermercado .... [by car]

e) Voy al polideportivo .... [by bike]

f) Voy de vacaciones .... [by plane]

g) Voy a Francia .... [by boat]

Getting to school is much more fun since we moved to the Lake District.

I would walk 500 miles — actually, I would rather take the train...

Some of these words are <u>easier to learn</u> than others because they sound similar to English — so it probably <u>makes sense</u> to spend more time learning the <u>trickier ones</u>. Afterwards you can treat yourself to a biscuit...

Transport

Q1   Unscramble the words in these Spanish sentences using the English translations to help you.

a) ¿sale Málaga para tren cuándo el? *[When does the train to Malaga leave?]*

....

b) ¿andén tren qué de el sale? *[Which platform does the train leave from?]*

....

c) seis el del número sale andén tren. *[The train leaves from platform six.]*

....

d) ¿a tren Málaga llega cuándo el? *[When does the train arrive in Malaga?]*

....

Q2   Write in Spanish how you would ask for these train tickets. Use the example to help you.

KEY

→	⇄	1°	2°
single	return	first class	second class

a) VALENCIA 2° →   *Quisiera un billete de ida, de segunda clase, para Valencia.*

c) ÁVILA 1° ⇄ ....

b) SEGOVIA 1° → ....

d) CUENCA 2° ⇄ ....

Q3   Use the train timetable to answer the questions below in Spanish.   "¿Adónde?" means "Where (to)?"

a) ¿A qué hora sale el tren para Sevilla?   ....

b) ¿De qué andén sale el tren para Granada?   ....

c) ¿Adónde va el tren que sale a las cuatro?   ....

d) ¿A qué hora sale el tren para Almería?   ....

e) ¿Adónde va el tren que sale a la una y cinco? ....

f) ¿De qué andén sale el tren para Murcia?   ....

Destino	Salida	Andén
Granada	9.10	5
Sevilla	10.30	6
Murcia	11.45	1
Málaga	1.05	3
Córdoba	4.00	8
Almería	5.15	2

Post Office and Telephones

Q1   These Spanish words for things you might find in the post office have been scrambled. Write them correctly then match them up to the correct word in English.

a) nu lesol   ....*un sello*............   *a letter*

b) aun atcra   ....   *an envelope*

c) uan slopat   ....   *a postbox*

d) nu nuzób   ....   *a postcard*

e) la icróndice ....   *the address*

f) un ebros   ....   *a stamp*

> I wish these came in strawberry flavour...

Q2   Read this conversation in a Spanish post office and answer the questions in English.

Kate:	**Hola. Quisiera un sello para Alemania. ¿Cuánto cuesta?**
Cajero:	**Cuesta un euro con cincuenta, señorita.**
Kate:	**También quisiera un sobre.**
Cajero:	**Por supuesto. Cuesta dos euros en total.**
Kate:	**Muchas gracias. ¿Dónde está el buzón por favor?**
Cajero:	**A la izquierda.**

'Cajero' means 'cashier'.

a) What is the first thing Kate asks for? ....

b) How much does this cost? ....

c) What else does Kate want to buy? ....

d) What is the final question Kate asks? ....

Q3   These people are on the phone. For each person, write out what they are saying in Spanish.

> My telephone number is 23 54 91.

Gabriela

> Hello, it's Vicente.

Vicente

> Can I speak to Philip please?

Lizzie

a) Gabriela: ....

b) Vicente: ....

c) Lizzie: ....

Informal Letters

Q1   Here are some phrases from informal letters, but some of the words are missing.
      Choose from the words on the right to complete each sentence.

      a) Thanks for your letter.   .... por tu ....

      b) Dear John, ... John,

      c) A hug   Un ....

      d) How are you?   ¿Qué ....?

      e) Write soon.   .... pronto.

> escríbeme   carta
> tal   gracias
> abrazo   querido

Q2   Yolanda wants to write to her friend Santi but she's got all the phrases in the wrong order.
      Choose a phrase from the list to complete the missing parts of the letter.

      a) ....

    b) ....

    c) ....

    Yo estoy muy bien. ¡Mañana voy de vacaciones!

    d) ....

      e) ....

Letter Phrases

Me alegró mucho oír de ti.

Yolanda

Querido Santi,

Bilbao, 20 de agosto

Hasta pronto.

Q3   Now it's your turn. Write an informal letter to your friend Ana, including the details below.

   • The date and place of writing

   • Greet Ana

   • Ask her how she is

   • Thank her for her letter

   • Tell her to write soon

   • Send her best wishes

   • Sign your name

....

....

....

....

....

....

....

....

Section 6 — Phone Calls and Letters

Formal Letters

Q1 In the box are some useful phrases for writing formal letters.
Write the number of the phrase you would use:

a) to write to a woman whose name you know ....

b) to write the place and date of writing ....

c) to write to a man whose name you don't know ....

d) to sign off your letter 'yours faithfully' ....

1)	**Estimada señora...**
2)	**Muy señora mía**
3)	**Muy señor mío**
4)	**Crewe, 20 de mayo**
5)	**Le saluda atentamente**
6)	**Hasta pronto**

Q2 Read Al's letter then write 'T' for true and 'F' for false next to each statement (a-f).

> **10 Cashew Street,**
> **Nutsville.**
> **18 de septiembre**
>
> **Muy señor mío,**
>
> **Quisiera una parcela para una tienda para doce días, desde el 5 hasta el 16 de junio. ¿Cuánto cuesta, por favor?**
>
> **Le saluda atentamente,**
> **Al Mund**

a) Al knows the name of the person he's writing to. ☐

b) Al wants to book a hotel room. ☐

c) He wants to stay for 14 nights. ☐

d) He wants to stay in June. ☐

e) He asks how much it will cost. ☐

f) Al signs off his letter with 'best wishes'. ☐

So many letters...

Q3 Using the letter in question 2 as a model, write your own letter to make a hotel reservation. Include all of these details:

- Your address

- The date of writing

- Greet Señora Domínguez, the hotel owner

- Say you would like to stay from 5th to 9th August

- Say you would like two double rooms

- Ask how much it costs

- Sign off your letter

....
....
....
....
....
....
....
....

Weather and Seasons

Q1 Write the English for these types of weather.

a) Hace buen tiempo → ....

b) Hay niebla → ....

c) Hace viento → ....

d) Hace frío → ....

e) Hace mal tiempo → ....

f) Hace mucho calor → ....

Q2 Fill in the gaps with 'hace', 'está' or 'hay'.

a) .... sol

b) .... lloviendo

c) ....calor

d) .... nevando

e) .... tormenta

f) .... nublado

Q3 Here's a map of Spain. Write down what the weather is like in each place in Spanish.

a) En Barcelona ....

b) En Málaga ....

c) En Bilbao ....

d) En Madrid ....

e) En Sevilla ....

f) En Valencia ....

Q4 Fill in the correct season from the box to complete each sentence.

la primavera	el invierno	el otoño	el verano

a) Julio es un mes en ....

b) Diciembre es un mes en ....

c) Octubre es un mes en ....

d) Abril es un mes en ....

Holidays

Q1 Match each question about holidays with the answer by putting a number in the box. I've done the first one for you.

a) ¿Adónde vas de vacaciones normalmente? [4]

b) ¿Con quién vas de vacaciones? [ ]

c) ¿Cómo vas? [ ]

d) ¿Cuánto tiempo pasas allí? [ ]

e) ¿Dónde te quedas? [ ]

f) ¿Qué haces allí? [ ]

g) ¿Qué tiempo hace? [ ]

1) **Voy en avión.**
2) **Hace calor.**
3) **Hago ciclismo.**
4) ~~**Normalmente voy a Francia.**~~
5) **Voy con mi familia.**
6) **Paso dos semanas allí.**
7) **Me quedo en un albergue juvenil.**

Q2 Read what Marisol has written about her holidays, then answer the questions below in English.

¡Hola! Normalmente voy de vacaciones al sur de Portugal. Voy en coche con mi madre, mi padrastro y mi hermano. Paso dos semanas en un hotel. Hay una piscina pero prefiero nadar en el mar. Hace mucho calor y me gusta leer en la playa.

a) Where does she normally go? ....
b) Who does she go with? ....
c) How does she get there? ....
d) How long does she go for? ....
e) Where does she stay? ....
f) What is the weather like? ....

Q3 Answer the questions in Spanish. Use the English translation to help you.

a) ¿Adónde vas de vacaciones normalmente? ....
[Normally I go to Italy.]

b) ¿Con quién vas de vacaciones? ....
[I go with my friends.]

c) ¿Cuánto tiempo pasas allí? ....
[I spend ten days there.]

d) ¿Qué tiempo hace? ....
[It's hot and sunny.]

Hotels and Camping

Q1 Write each Spanish word from the box next to the correct English translation.

| la tienda | la caravana | el saco de dormir | el agua potable | la parcela |

a) .... = caravan

b) .... = sleeping bag

c) .... = drinking water

d) .... = tent

e) .... = pitch

Q2 Write down in Spanish how you would describe the rooms below. I've done the first one for you.

a) *Una habitación individual con ducha.* ....

b) ....

c) ....

d) ....

e) ....

Q3 Write these words out in Spanish. Don't forget to include 'el', 'la', 'los' or 'las' for each one.

a) hotel ....

b) key ....

c) room ....

d) telephone ....

e) youth hostel ....

f) campsite ....

g) dining room ....

h) toilets ....

Sleeping in a bag? — No thanks, I'd rather have a feather duvet...

You may think, "I <u>hate camping</u> so I'll <u>never need</u> to know any of this <u>camping vocab</u>", but you'd be wrong. You need it for KS3 Spanish — and for that <u>camping trip to Spain</u> your family are secretly planning...

Booking Accommodation

Q1 Read these two letters, then put 'P' (for Peter) and 'E' (for Emma) next to each statement.

> Quisiera reservar una habitación individual con baño. Me quedo una semana del once al dieciocho de julio.
> Peter

> Quisiera reservar una parcela para una tienda. Me quedo dos semanas, del seis al veinte de agosto.
> Emma

a) I'm going camping. ☐

b) I want to be able to have a bath. ☐

c) I'm staying for one week. ☐

d) I'm going in August. ☐

Q2 Pablo is in a hotel in Spain. Read the conversation and fill in the gaps with the correct word from the box below.

tres	baño	llave	euros	individual	cuántas

PABLO: Buenos días. ¿Tiene una habitación ....?

RECEPCIONISTA: Sí. ¿La quiere con ducha o con .... ?

PABLO: Con ducha por favor.

RECEPCIONISTA: Muy bien. ¿ .... noches quiere quedarse?

PABLO: .... noches. ¿Cuánto cuesta?

RECEPCIONISTA: Por noche cuesta sesenta ....

PABLO: Bueno, la quiero.

RECEPCIONISTA: Aquí tiene la ....

Q3 Write these sentences in Spanish.

a) Do you have a free pitch? →

b) I'd like a pitch for a caravan. →

c) I would like to stay for 5 nights. →

How do you ask for a room with a queen-sized bed and a plasma TV...

Teachers love to talk about holidays, so if you know all the answers to these questions, you'll survive. If not, you'd better go back and practise — you don't want to be the person who thinks 'tienda' just means 'shop'...

Countries

Q1 Draw lines to match the Spanish words on the left with the English words on the right.

Gran Bretaña	Scotland
Inglaterra	Great Britain
Escocia	United Kingdom
País de Gales	Northern Ireland
Irlanda del Norte	England
Reino Unido	Wales

Q2 Where do these people live? Write the answer in English. I've done the first one for you.

a) Vivo en Holanda. ......*Holland*...........

b) Vivo en Alemania. ....

c) Vivo en Irlanda. ....

d) Vivo en Suiza. ....

e) Vivo en Bélgica. ....

f) Vivo en Francia. ....

Q3 Write down what these people would say about themselves in Spanish. I've done the first one for you.

a) Marco lives in Italy. *Vivo en Italia.*

b) Pablo lives in Portugal.

c) Anabel lives in Spain.

d) Hans lives in Austria.

Q4 Which country is being described? Answer in Spanish.

a) The capital city is Paris and the people eat lots of cheese. ....

b) The capital city is Madrid and the country is famous for paella. ....

c) The capital city is Rome and this country eats lots of pizza and pasta. ....

Nationalities

Q1 Read the following statements. Write the person's nationality in English and circle the correct symbol to show whether they're male 🚹 or female 🚺. I've done the first one for you.

a) Soy holandés. ......*Dutch*...... (🚹) 🚺

b) Soy francesa. .... 🚹 🚺

c) Soy española. .... 🚹 🚺

d) Soy norirlandés. .... 🚹 🚺

e) Soy galesa. .... 🚹 🚺

f) Soy escocés. .... 🚹 🚺

g) Soy italiano. .... 🚹 🚺

h) Soy alemana. .... 🚹 🚺

Q2 Imagine that you are each of these people. Write down how you would describe your nationality in Spanish. I've done the first one for you.

a)
Chloe — English   .....*Soy inglesa.*.....

b)
Patrick — Irish   ....

c)
Amélie — French   ....

d)
David — Spanish   ....

e)
Anna — Italian   ....

f)
Gareth — Welsh   ....

Q3 Read this email. Write a 'T' for true or an 'F' for false next to each statement.

¡Hola! Vivo en la capital de España. Soy española. Mi madre es irlandesa y mi padre es español. Mi mejor amiga se llama Beth. Es escocesa. Mi profesor de biología es galés y mi profesora de geografía es alemana.

The person who wrote this...

a) ...is a boy. ☐

b) ...lives in Spain. ☐

c) ...has a mother who's Irish. ☐

d) ...has a best friend who's French. ☐

e) ...has a biology teacher who is Welsh. ☐

f) ...has a geography teacher who's English. ☐

Opinions

Q1 Use the key to write opinions in Spanish about the school subjects below. The first one has been done for you.

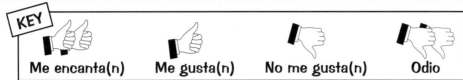

KEY

Me encanta(n)   Me gusta(n)   No me gusta(n)   Odio

a) el español

    Me encanta el español.

b) el dibujo

    ....

c) la geografía

    ....

d) la informática

    ....

e) las ciencias

    ....

f) las matemáticas

    ....

Q2 Fill in the missing letters to complete these Spanish opinion words. Use the English translation to help you.

a) interesting → i __ te __ es __ nt __

b) easy → fá __ il

c) fun → d __ ver __ __ do

d) boring → __ b __ rri __ o

e) strange → __ a __ o

f) difficult → d __ fíci __

g) great → __ st __ pe __ __ o

h) good → b __ e __ o

i) awful → __ orr __ __ le

j) beautiful → p __ __ ci __ so

Q3 Write out these sentences in Spanish. The first one has been done for you.

a) I don't like chess because it's difficult.

    No me gusta el ajedrez porque es difícil.

b) I like listening to the radio because it's interesting.

    ....

c) I hate washing the car because it's awful.

    ....

d) I love sports because they're fun.

    ....

Asking Questions

Q1 Match each English word to the correct Spanish word.
Then choose the correct Spanish question word to complete each question (a-g).

How?   ¿Cuándo?
When?   ¿Dónde?
Which?   ¿Quién?
How much?   ¿Cómo?
Where?   ¿Cuál?
Who?   ¿Qué?
What?   ¿Cuánto?

a) ¿............... hay en tu dormitorio?
b) ¿............... te levantas?
c) ¿............... es tu color preferido?
d) ¿ _Cómo_ te llamas?
e) ¿............... quiere tarta?
f) ¿............... cuesta?
g) ¿............... está Kelis?

Q2 What do the following questions mean in English?

a) ¿Cuándo es tu cumpleaños? ....
b) ¿Cuánto cuesta una limonada? ....
c) ¿Dónde vive Sandra? ....
d) ¿A qué hora comes? ....
e) ¿Cómo está tu madre? ....
f) ¿Quién es Alexis? ....

Q3 Read these answers, then write down what the question would be in Spanish.
Use the question words in Q1 to start your questions.

a) Vivo en Valencia.   _¿Dónde vives?_
b) Me llamo Malik. ....
c) El libro cuesta cinco euros. ....
d) El tren sale a las cuatro y media. ....
e) Voy al instituto en autobús. ....
f) En my dormitorio hay una cama. ....

Questions about questions — who came up with that idea?
Ah yes, you do need to learn lots of question words for this page. And get to grips with those funny looking question marks. But on the bright side, then **YOU** can be the one asking all the questions. Muah ha ha...

Words for People and Objects

Q1 For each of these words write in the box whether each word is masculine (M) or feminine (F).

a) el gato ☐   d) un melocotón ☐   g) el buzón ☐

b) la silla ☐   e) el jarabe ☐   h) la nariz ☐

c) una manzana ☐   f) la casa ☐   i) una cama ☐

Q2 Change the following words into plurals.

a) un perro → dos ....   g) una bicicleta → dos ....

b) una pera → dos ....   h) un tomate → dos ....

c) una granja → dos ....   i) una revista → dos ....

d) un armario → dos ....   j) un vestido → dos ....

e) un primo → dos ....   k) un parque → dos ....

f) una calle → dos ....   l) una clase → dos ....

Q3 Now change these words into plurals. Remember that if there's an accent on the last vowel, the accent disappears when the word becomes plural.

a) un tren → dos ....   e) un árbol → dos ....

b) una actriz → dos ....   f) un melón → dos ....

c) un ratón → dos ....   g) un lápiz → dos ....

d) un yogur → dos ....   h) una nariz → dos ....

Q4 Complete these sentences by writing each word in brackets in its plural form.

a) Tengo cuatro [hermana] ....

b) Miguel come muchos [plátano] ....

c) Mi tío tiene ocho [coche] ....

d) Mis primos son [albañil] ....

e) En mi casa hay seis [habitación] ....

f) En la pastelería hay muchos [pastel] ....

g) En nuestro salón tenemos dos [sillón] ....

How to say 'The' and 'A'

Q1   Rewrite these Spanish words with 'el', 'la', 'los' or 'las'.

a) una tortuga   ......*la tortuga*............   f) una tirita   ....

b) unas revistas   ....   g) unos actores ....

c) un médico   ....   h) un restaurante ....

d) unas corbatas   ....   i) unas reglas   ....

e) un bocadillo   ....   j) una trompeta ....

Q2   Circle the correct option to complete these sentences.

a) El banco está enfrente **del** / **de la** supermercado.

b) El cine está al lado **del** / **de la** farmacia.

c) Para ir **al** / **a la** banco, tome la primera calle **al** / **a la** derecha.

d) La estación está **al** / **a la** final **del** / **de la** calle.

e) Para ir **al** / **a la** playa, tome la segunda calle **al** / **a la** izquierda.

de + el = del

Q3   Write out this English shopping list in Spanish.

I need some custard, some raisins and some curry sauce....

a bottle of water

some potatoes

some eggs

some bananas

an onion

a peach

una botella de agua
....
....
....
....
....
....

Q4   Write out these English sentences in Spanish.

a) I don't have any pets. → .....*No tengo animales en casa.*.................................

b) I don't have any brothers. → ....

c) I don't have a pen. → ....

d) I don't have any money. → ....

I, You, Hím, Them...

Q1 Complete the table using the Spanish subject pronouns from the box below. *All these 'you's are <u>familiar</u>.*

she	you (singular)	I	we	they (feminine)	you (plural)	he	they (masculine)
....	....	....	....	....	....	....	....

> nosotros   él   yo   ellas   tú   vosotros   ella   ellos

Q2 Complete these sentences with the correct subject pronoun for each person.

a) <u>Sara</u> vive en Madrid. → ......*Ella*...... vive en Madrid.

b) <u>Jorge</u> tiene ocho años. → .... tiene ocho años.

c) <u>Evita y Célia</u> están en la playa. → .... están en la playa.

d) <u>Mis hermanos</u> juegan al fútbol. → .... juegan al fútbol.

e) <u>Mi padre y yo</u> vamos de compras. → .... vamos de compras.

f) <u>David y tú</u> sois tímidos. → .... sois tímidos.

Q3 Complete each sentence using the correct direct object pronoun from the box.

a) My grandmother visits <u>us</u>. → Mi abuela .... visita.

b) Janice and Deborah see <u>me</u>. → Janice y Deborah .... ven.

c) I know <u>you</u> (singular). → .... conozco.

d) I'm looking at <u>you</u> (plural). → .... miro.

> **DIRECT OBJECT PRONOUNS**
> me   te
> nos   os

Q4 Complete each sentence using the correct direct object pronoun from the box.

a) Mi madre limpia <u>la casa</u>. → Mi madre .... limpia.

b) Ellos lavan <u>los coches</u>. → Ellos .... lavan.

c) Rafael compra <u>unas manzanas</u>. → Rafael .... compra.

d) Natalia quiere <u>unos zapatos</u>. → Natalia .... quiere.

e) Nosotros bebemos <u>el zumo</u>. → Nosotros .... bebemos.

> **DIRECT OBJECT PRONOUNS**
> lo   la
> los   las

<u>She said to us what she said you said to them, so we said to him...</u>
<u>Pronouns</u> can be pretty darn <u>handy</u> but if you're not clear on them, they can cause a <u>right muddle</u>. Make sure you learn all the pronouns <u>really well</u> so you can feel confident using them — and be a <u>Pronoun Pro</u>.

Words to Describe Things

Q1   Fill in the missing forms of these adjectives to complete the table.

masculine singular	feminine singular	masculine plural	feminine plural
pequeño	....	pequeños	pequeñas
alto	alta	....	altas
viejo	....	viejos	....
....	blanca	....	....
....	....	....	bonitas

Q2   Complete the following sentences using the correct form of the adjective in brackets.

a) Mi casa no es muy .... _[grande]_

b) Las sillas son .... _[raro]_

c) Mi amiga es .... _[inteligente]_

d) Mi hermana es .... _[trabajador]_

e) Estos deberes son .... _[difícil]_

f) Mis pantalones son .... _[verde]_ y .... _[largo]_

g) Mi primo es .... _[horrible]_ pero mi tía es .... _[simpático]_

h) Tengo dos lápices .... _[rojo]_ y un bolígrafo .... _[negro]_

Q3   Complete these sentences to translate what each person says in Spanish.

Luisa

Augustín

Rodolfo

Ornella

Luisa: Llevo ....

Augustín: Me gustan ....

Rodolfo: Quiero ....

Ornella: Tengo ....

Making Comparisons

Q1 Complete these sentences in Spanish. Make sure all parts of the sentence agree with the noun.

a) German is less difficult. → El alemán es ....

b) Those cats are the fattest. → Esos gatos son...

c) This class is the easiest. → Esta clase es ....

d) My book is less interesting. → Mi libro es ....

e) Tim's glasses are the biggest. → Las gafas de Tim son ....

Q2 Complete these sentences in Spanish. Use the vocab in the box to help you.

> bueno → mejor   malo → peor   viejo → mayor   joven → menor

a) Marcos es *[young]* .... pero Pablito es *[younger]* ....

Su hermana Romina es *[the youngest]* ....

b) La historia es *[bad]* .... pero el inglés es *[worse]* ....

El dibujo es *[the worst]* ....

c) Mi ratón es *[old]* .... pero mi gato es *[older]* ....

Mi perro es *[the oldest]* ....

d) Tu postre es *[good]* .... pero su postre es *[better]* ....

Mi postre es *[the best]* ....

Q3 These funny-looking folk are all different heights.
Use the comparison phrases in the box to complete the sentences in Spanish.

> más .... que
>
> menos .... que
>
> tan .... como

Neil   Grizelda   Bob   Carlos

a) Carlos es .... *más alto que* .... Grizelda.

b) Grizelda es .... Bob.

c) Bob es .... Neil.

d) Neil es .... Carlos.

'My' and 'Your' — 'This' and 'These'

Q1 Complete each sentence using the correct possessive adjective: '**mi**', '**tu**' or '**su**'. Remember that these words change for plural nouns.

a) My sister is a nurse. .... hermana es enfermera.

b) Your ears are very big. .... orejas son muy grandes.

c) Where are his parents? ¿Dónde están .... padres?

d) My shoes are very comfortable. .... zapatos son muy cómodos.

e) Is their homework difficult? ¿.............. deberes son difíciles?

f) Your books are on her bed. .... libros están en .... cama.

g) My uncle is your teacher. .... tío es .... profesor.

> Thank you, Harold, I had them hand-made in Texas.

Q2 Now complete these sentences using either '**nuestro**' or '**vuestro**'. These words change depending on whether a noun is masculine, feminine, singular or plural.

a) Our grandmother is intelligent. .... abuela es inteligente.

b) Your houses are nearby. .... casas están cerca.

c) Our dogs are friendly. .... perros son simpáticos.

d) Your cousins live with our cousins. .... primos viven con .... primas.

e) Our mum and your dad are actors. .... madre y .... padre son actores.

Q3 Complete these tables using the Spanish words for 'this', 'that', 'these' and 'those'.

the book	el libro
this book	....
that book	*ese libro*
these books	....
those books	....

the shirt	la camisa
this shirt	*esta camisa*
that shirt	....
these shirts	....
those shirts	....

Q4 Complete these sentences in Spanish using the English sentences to help.

a) That banana is your (singular) banana. → .... plátano es .... plátano.

b) These pears are my pears. → .... peras son .... peras.

c) Those boys are her brothers. → .... chicos son .... hermanos.

'Por' and 'Para'

Q1   Read these pairs of sentences and tick the box to show which uses '**por**' and '**para**' correctly.

a)
| Voy a la piscina por nadar. ☐ |
| Voy a la piscina para nadar. ☐ |

d)
| Pago siete euros por la entrada. ☐ |
| Pago siete euros para la entrada. ☐ |

b)
| El coche pasa por el túnel. ☐ |
| El coche pasa para el túnel. ☐ |

e)
| El tren para Girona sale a la una. ☐ |
| El tren por Girona sale a la una. ☐ |

c)
| El libro es por ti. ☐ |
| El libro es para ti. ☐ |

f)
| Voy al centro por la mañana. ☐ |
| Voy al centro para la mañana. ☐ |

Q2   For each sentence, write '**por**' or '**para**' to translate the underlined word.

a) the train <u>to</u> Barcelona ....

b) she left <u>in</u> the afternoon ....

c) the cake is <u>for</u> you ....

d) 3 euros <u>for</u> one ice cream ....

e) We went <u>through</u> the park ....

f) she's going <u>for</u> three days ....

g) thank you <u>for</u> your letter ....

h) I want it <u>by</u> tomorrow ....

i) he plays <u>in</u> the morning ....

j) the coach <u>to</u> London ....

Q3   Complete these sentences in Spanish, using either '**por**' or '**para**'.

a) Is there a train to Valencia?   ¿Hay un tren .... Valencia?

b) He paid two euros for the pen.   Pagó dos euros .... el bolígrafo.

c) I go to the park to play football.   Voy al parque .... jugar al fútbol.

d) I washed the car in the afternoon.   Lavé el coche .... la tarde.

e) The fish is for you.   El pescado es .... ti.

f) Thanks for the book.   Gracias .... el libro.

g) The girls went through the bakery.   Las chicas fueron .... la panadería.

I thought pandas only ate bamboo...

I hope this page doesn't para-lyse your brain...
I know this is difficult. I'm sorry. But don't let it <u>put you off</u> Spanish. Why not go and listen to some Spanish language hits as a <u>reward</u> for your hard work? You can't beat a bit of 'La Bamba' to cheer you up...

Verbs in the Present Tense

Q1   Write out '**beber**' in the present tense — be careful, the pronouns have been jumbled up. Use the verb table for 'comer' to help you.

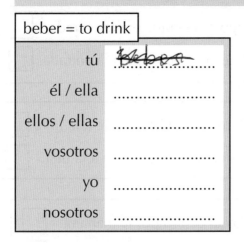

beber = to drink	
tú	~~bebes~~
él / ella	....
ellos / ellas	....
vosotros	....
yo	....
nosotros	....

comer = to eat	
yo	com**o**
tú	com**es**
él / ella	com**e**
nosotros	com**emos**
vosotros	com**éis**
ellos / ellas	com**en**

Whoever said marathons were easy was lying. I...need...water...

Q2   Look at the verb table for '**hablar**', then write out the correct present tense forms of these verbs.

hablar = to speak	
yo	habl**o**
tú	habl**as**
él / ella	habl**a**
nosotros	habl**amos**
vosotros	habl**áis**
ellos / ellas	habl**an**

a) Nosotros .... *[bailar]* mucho.

b) Ella .... *[dibujar]* muy bien.

c) Yo .... *[escuchar]* la radio cada día.

d) Ellos .... *[cantar]* muy mal.

e) Vosotros .... *[trabajar]* poco.

f) ¿Tú .... *[nadar]* cada semana?

Q3   Use the example for '**vivir**' to write the correct verb from the circle next to the pronoun.

a) Yo..

b) Tú..

c) Él / ella.......................................

d) Nosotros....................................

e) Vosotros ....

f) Ellos / ellas ....

recibo
deciden
abrimos
partes
escribís
sube

vivir = to live	
yo	viv**o**
tú	viv**es**
él / ella	viv**e**
nosotros	viv**imos**
vosotros	viv**ís**
ellos / ellas	viv**en**

Q4   Put each of these Spanish verbs in the correct form of the present tense.

a) Mi amigo y yo .... *[cantar]*

b) Yo .... *[asistir]*

c) Fabián .... *[correr]*

d) Emilia ....*[aprender]*

e) Vosotros .... *[decidir]*

f) Tú .... *[ayudar]*

Verbs in the Present Tense

Q1 Choose the correct form of 'querer' from the circle to fill in the gaps in these sentences.

Circle words: quieren, queréis, quiere, quieres, quiero, queremos

a) Él .... comer patatas.
b) Ellos .... comer pizza.
c) Yo .... comer ensalada.
d) ¿Tú .... comer pescado?
e) Nosotros .... comer pasta.
f) Vosotros .... comer mariscos.

Q2 Write the correct form of 'tener' in the present tense. *These are familiar 'you's.*

a) I have ....
b) They have ....
c) You (singular) have ....
d) You (plural) have ....
e) He has ....
f) We have ....

Q3 Write these sentences in Spanish using the correct form of 'poder'. Use the words in the box to help you. I've done the first one. *These are familiar 'you's.*

a) I can listen to music. *Puedo escuchar música.*
b) We can drink water. ....
c) He can play football. ....
d) They can play the flute. ....
e) You (singular) can swim. ....
f) You (plural) can read. ....
g) I can speak French. ....

Useful vocab
beber agua
escuchar música
leer
hablar francés
tocar la flauta
jugar al fútbol
nadar

Q4 Read the following text then answer the questions below in English.

Hola, me llamo Lara. Tengo dos hermanas. Mis hermanas tienen catorce y dieciséis años. Mis hermanas y yo tenemos un gato, Bopi. Quiero vivir en Inglaterra en el futuro porque puedo hablar inglés.

a) How many sisters does Lara have? ....
b) How old are they? ....
c) What do Lara and her sisters have? ....
d) Why does Lara want to live in England in the future? ....

Section 8 — Grammar and Phrases

Irregular Verbs in the Present Tense

Q1 Write down which verb is used in each of these sentences.
Choose from 'ser', 'estar' and 'ir'. I've done the first one for you.

a) Estamos en la playa. ....*estar*........

e) Voy al supermercado. ....

b) Mañana vamos de compras. ....

f) Somos dos chicas inglesas. ....

c) Hoy estoy muy cansado. ....

g) Mis gatos son blancos. ....

d) David es delgado. ....

h) Edimburgo está en Escocia. ....

Q2 Fill in the gaps with the correct present tense form of the irregular verb in the brackets.

a) Yo .... [estar] en Madrid.

e) Tú.................... [ser] alto.

b) Olivia .... [ser] profesora.

f) Yo .... [ir] a la piscina.

c) Iago y Nacho .... [ir] al cine.

g) Ellos .... [ser] españoles.

d) Jorge .... [estar] muy contento.

h) Ana y yo .... [estar] en el parque.

Q3 Javier is writing a letter to his new penfriend, María. Fill in the gaps
with the correct form of the present tense verb in brackets.

Querida María,

¿Cómo .... [estar — tú]? Yo .... [estar — yo] muy bien.

.... [ser — yo] alumno en el instituto. Estudio muchas asignaturas pero me

gusta el español porque el profesor .... [ser — él] simpático. Mi amigo y yo

.... [ir — nosotros] al instituto en coche, pero otros alumnos

.... [ir — ellos] en bicicleta porque .... [ser — ellos] deportistas.

Hasta pronto, Javier.

Q4 Circle either 'hay' or 'es' to complete these sentences correctly.

a) En mi estuche **hay / es** un lápiz que **hay / es** gris.

b) Mi dormitorio **hay / es** grande pero la cocina **hay / es** pequeña.

c) En mi dormitorio **hay / es** una cama, una mesa y una silla, pero no **hay / es** televisión.

d) La historia **hay / es** muy aburrida pero el inglés **hay / es** muy interesante.

e) **Hay / es** muchos museos en Londres porque **hay / es** la capital de Inglaterra.

'Ser' and 'Estar'

Q1 Decide whether the sentences below use '**ser**' or '**estar**' and write the letter in the table. The first one's been done.

SER	ESTAR
a	

a) She is Spanish.

b) He is my brother.

c) I am ill.

d) My mother is sad today.

e) David is a police officer.

f) Cara is in Valencia.

g) His eyes are green.

h) He is intelligent.

Q2 Tick the box next to the correct sentence in each pair.

a) Su pelo es negro. ☐
Su pelo está negro. ☐

b) Mi hermano es muy contento hoy. ☐
Mi hermano está muy contento hoy. ☐

c) Madrid está en el centro de España. ☐
Madrid es en el centro de España. ☐

d) Mi padre es médico. ☐
Mi padre está médico. ☐

e) Somos en el parque. ☐
Estamos en el parque. ☐

f) Estoy muy triste. ☐
Soy muy triste. ☐

Q3 Complete these sentences using the correct form of either '**ser**' or '**estar**'. These are <u>familiar</u> 'you's.

a) **My uncle is a mechanic.** = Mi tío .... mecánico.

b) **He is hardworking.** = ... trabajador.

c) **I am ill.** = ... enfermo.

d) **They are in the restaurant.** = ... en el restaurante.

e) **Her eyes are blue.** = Sus ojos .... azules.

f) **Grizebeck is in England.** = Grizebeck .... en Inglaterra.

g) **You (singular) are sporty.** = ...deportista.

h) **This is my mother.** = Esta .... mi madre.

Be&Be — would you like a single or double room, señor?
Knowing when to use '<u>ser</u>' and '<u>estar</u>' has got to be one of the most <u>complicated</u> Spanish rules ever.
But if you use '<u>ser</u>' for <u>permanent things</u> and '<u>estar</u>' for stuff that <u>might change in the future</u>, you'll be <u>fine</u>.

Reflexive Verbs

Q1   Draw lines to match the pictures with the Spanish phrases. I've done the first one for you.

a)

Me acuesto

Me levanto

b)

Me despierto

Me lavo los dientes

c)

Me visto

Me ducho

d)

e)

f)

Q2   Write the correct pronoun from the box to complete each reflexive verb.

a)   .... levanta

b)   .... vestimos

c)   .... duchas

d)   .... acuestan

e)   .... despertáis

f)   .... lavo

me	nos
te	os
se	se

Q3   What does David do at different times of the day? Write a sentence in Spanish to describe what he does. Use the verb and time in brackets to help you.

a) David wakes up. *[despertarse — 7am]* .... *David se despierta a las siete.* ....

b) David gets up. *[levantarse — 7.15am]* ....

c) David gets showered. *[ducharse — 7.30am]* ....

d) David goes to bed. *[acostarse — 10.15pm]* ....

   Don't forget, 'acostarse' is an 'o to ue' stem-changing verb.

Q4   Now write these sentences in Spanish. Use the verbs in brackets to help.   These are <u>familiar</u> 'you's.

a) I get up. *[levantarse]* .... *Me levanto.* ....

b) He cleans his teeth. *[lavarse los dientes]* ....

c) You (singular) have a shower. *[ducharse]* ....

d) You (plural) get washed. *[lavarse]* ....

e) We go to sleep. *[acostarse]* ....

f) They get dressed. *[vestirse]* ....

Remember — 'vestirse' is an 'e' to 'i' stem-changing verb.

<u>Making Sentences Negative</u>

Q1   Read the following information about Sara, then decide if the statements are true or false. Write 'T' for 'true' or 'F' for false in the box next to each statement.

> Me llamo Sara. Soy española.
> Mi mejor amiga es francesa
> pero no hablo francés. Me
> gusta escuchar música y bailar.
> No me gusta ver películas y
> no voy nunca al cine. Vivo en
> un pueblo pequeño y aburrido,
> pero me gusta mi casa.

a) Sara isn't Spanish. ☐

b) Sara doesn't speak French. ☐

c) She likes listening to music and dancing. ☐

d) She never goes to the cinema. ☐

e) She lives in a large town. ☐

f) She doesn't like her house. ☐

Q2   Make the following sentences negative. Use the example to help you.

a) Soy profesor. ➡ *No soy profesor.*
[I'm not a teacher.]

b) Me lavo los dientes. ➡ ....
[I don't brush my teeth.]

c) Tenemos dinero. ➡ ....
[We don't have any money.]

d) Quiero ver la película. ➡ ....
[I don't want to watch the film.]

e) Van al cine. ➡ ....
[They're not going to the cinema.]

f) Mi hermano es alto. ➡ ....
[My brother is not tall.]

g) Harry quiere leer. ➡ ....
[Harry doesn't want to read.]

Q3   Decide if the following sentences use '**nunca**' or '**nada**'. Circle the correct answer.

a) I never go to the swimming pool. = No voy **nunca / nada** a la piscina.

b) We never talk in class. = No hablamos **nunca / nada** en clase.

c) I don't eat anything for breakfast. = No como **nunca / nada** para el desayuno.

d) You never listen to me. = No me escuchas **nunca / nada**.

e) He doesn't do anything at the weekends. = No hace **nunca / nada** los fines de semana.

f) I don't see anything. = No veo **nunca / nada**.

Talking about the Future

Q1 Draw lines to match up the Spanish on the left with the English meaning on the right.

Voy a comer	**We are going to eat.**
Vamos a comer	**You** (singular) **are going to eat.**
Vas a comer	**I am going to eat.**
Vais a comer	**He / she is going to eat.**
Van a comer	**You** (plural) **are going to eat.**
Va a comer	**They are going to eat.**

Q2 Look at Alejandro's calendar for next week. Write a sentence describing what he is going to do each day. Use the example and the words in the box to help you.

lunes	martes	miércoles	jueves	viernes	sábado	domingo

a) El lunes   *va a tocar el piano.* ....

b) El martes ....

c) El miércoles ....

d) El jueves ....

e) El viernes ....

f) El sábado ....

g) El domingo ....

Useful vocab

hacer ciclismo

nadar

ir de compras

ver la televisión

~~tocar el piano~~

hacer senderismo

jugar al tenis

Q3 Complete these sentences in Spanish. The English is given in the brackets. These are <u>familiar</u> 'you's.

a) .... *[You (plural) are going to]* hacer los deberes.

b) .... *[We are going to]* hacer esquí.

c) .... *[They are going to]* jugar al baloncesto.

d) .... *[You (singular) are going to]* lavar el coche.

e) .... *[I am going to]* escuchar la radio.

f) .... *[He is not going to]* hacer footing.

g) .... *[I am not going to]* comer las galletas.

Giving Orders

Q1　Write down what these informal commands mean in English.
Use the infinitives in the box to help you.

a) **¡HABLA!**

b) **¡CAMINA!**

c) **¡EMPIEZA!**

....

....

....

d) **¡HAZ TUS DEBERES!**

e) **¡SÉ SIMPÁTICO!**

f) **¡VEN!**

....

....

....

ser [to be]
venir [to come]
hablar [to speak]
empezar [to start]
hacer [to do]
caminar [to walk]

Q2　Change these verbs into informal singular commands. Use the example to help you.

a) mirar = to look ......*¡mira!*......

e) escuchar = to listen ....

b) comer = to eat ....

f) correr = to run ....

c) saltar = to jump ....

g) ir = to go ....

d) abrir = to open ....

h) tener = to have ....

Don't forget, 'ir' and 'tener' are irregular.

Q3　Write a number from the box to match these Spanish formal
singular commands with the correct English translation.

a) ¡Venga! ☐

d) ¡Haga! ☐

b) ¡Tenga! ☐

e) ¡Vaya! ☐

c) ¡Coma! ☐

f) ¡Sea! ☐

1) Come!	4) Eat!
2) Go!	5) Do!
3) Be!	6) Have!

Q4　Now complete these formal singular commands. I've done the first one for you.

a) Wait here! = ¡......*Espere*...... [esperar] aquí!

You! Answer these questions, now!

b) Look at the board! = ¡...................... [mirar] la pizarra!

c) Listen to the music! = ¡...................... [escuchar] la música!

d) Open the window! = ¡...................... [abrir] la ventana!

e) Write a letter! = ¡...................... [escribir] una carta!

Talking about the Past

Q1 Rewrite each present tense verb in the past tense. They all follow the same pattern as '**hablar**'. The first one's been done for you.

a) Yo <u>ayudo</u> a mi madre. .... *ayudé* ....

b) Él <u>nada</u> en la piscina. ....

c) Tú <u>bailas</u> en la fiesta. ....

d) Nosotros <u>esquiamos</u> en Francia. ....

e) Vosotros <u>escucháis</u> la música. ....

f) Ellas <u>cantan</u> una canción. ....

hablar = to speak

yo =	habl<u>é</u>
tú =	habl<u>aste</u>
él / ella =	habl<u>ó</u>
nosotros =	habl<u>amos</u>
vosotros =	habl<u>asteis</u>
ellos / ellas =	habl<u>aron</u>

Q2 Use the verb table for '**beber**' to write each of these '**-er**' verbs in the past tense.

beber = to drink

yo =	beb<u>í</u>
tú =	beb<u>iste</u>
él / ella =	beb<u>ió</u>
nosotros =	beb<u>imos</u>
vosotros =	beb<u>isteis</u>
ellos / ellas =	beb<u>ieron</u>

a) Yo .... [comer] patatas fritas.

b) Ella .... [volver] el dos de mayo.

c) Nosotros .... [perder] todo el dinero.

d) ¿Tú .... [entender] el problema?

e) ¿Vosotros .... [aprender] mucho?

f) Ellos .... [correr] hasta la playa.

Q3 Write these past tense verbs in Spanish. These '**-ir**' verbs follow the same pattern as '**-er**' verbs — use the verb table for '**beber**' from question 2 to help you.

These are <u>familiar</u> 'you's.

a) I suffered ....[sufrir]

b) We wrote ....[escribir]

c) They went up ....[subir]

d) You (singular) opened ....[abrir]

e) He decided ....[decidir]

f) You (plural) lived ....[vivir]

Q4 Draw lines to match the Spanish with the English translation for these past tense verbs.

ir/ser — to go/to be	
fueron	I went/was
fue	they went/were
fui	you (singular) went/were
fuimos	we went/were
fuiste	you (plural) went/were
fuisteis	he/she went/was

hacer — to do	
hizo	you (plural) did
hiciste	I did
hicimos	he/she did
hicieron	we did
hice	you (singular) did
hicisteis	they did

Section 8 — Grammar and Phrases

Useful Small Words

Q1   Complete these sentences using either 'a' or 'de'.

a) **I'm going <u>to</u> Barcelona with my friend.** = Voy .... Barcelona con mi amigo.

b) **I bought two bottles <u>of</u> water.** = Compré dos botellas .... agua.

c) **My friend is <u>from</u> France.** = Mi amiga es .... Francia.

d) **A kilo <u>of</u> potatoes, please.** = Un kilo .... patatas, por favor.

e) **I've got a class <u>at</u> two o'clock.** = Tengo una clase .... las dos.

f) **We're going <u>to</u> Ireland tomorrow.** = Vamos .... Irlanda mañana.

g) **I want a cheese sandwich.** = Quiero un bocadillo ...... queso. ⬅ Don't forget, this is literally 'a sandwich <u>of</u> cheese'.

h) **The train leaves <u>at</u> 6:30.** = El tren sale .... las seis y media.

Q2   Choose either 'al' or 'a la', 'del' or 'de la' to complete each sentence. Circle the correct answer.

a) Vamos **al / a la** restaurante.

b) Voy **al / a la** banco.

c) Los actores son **de la / del** teatro.

d) Quiero ir **al / a la** piscina.

e) ¿El bolígrafo es **de la / del** profesor?

f) La carta es **de la / del** secretaria.

Q3   Complete these sentences with the correct preposition from the box. ⌐ Revise prepositions

~~sobre~~	en	detrás de	al lado de	delante de	debajo de

El gato está ....*sobre*.......... [on] la tienda.

La vaca está .... [behind] la tienda.

El hombre está .... [in] la tienda.

El ratón está .... [under] la vaca.

El perro está .... [next to] la tienda.

El fuego está .... [in front of] la tienda.

Small Linking Words

Q1 Make each pair of sentences into one sentence using
'**y**' or '**e**' (and). Use the example to help you.

a) Como una hamburguesa. Como un bocadillo. *Como una hamburguesa y un bocadillo.*

b) Hablamos francés. Hablamos inglés. ....

c) Diego compra patatas. Diego compra leche. ....

d) Sara es simpática. Sara es inteligente. ....

e) Pedro hace ciclismo. Pedro hace senderismo. ....

f) Hugo tiene un gato. Hugo tiene un pez. ....

Q2 Draw lines to match the beginning of each Spanish question
with the correct ending. I've done the first one for you.

¿Prefieres rojo   *o té?*

¿Juegas al fútbol   *o verde?*

¿Vas en tren   *o al parque?*

¿Quieres café   *o al tenis?*

¿Quieres escuchar música   *o en autobús?*

¿Vas al polideportivo   *o ver la televisión?*

Chocolate or vanilla?
Chocolate or vanilla?
Life is tough...

Q3 Use either '**pero**' (but) or '**porque**' (because) to complete these sentences.

a) Me gusta estudiar español .... es interesante.

b) Juego al hockey .... no juego al rugby.

c) Me gusta ir al cine .... prefiero ir al teatro.

d) Estudio matemáticas .... quiero ser profesor de matemáticas.

e) No me gustan las manzanas .... me encantan las peras.

f) Mi perro es muy bonito .... mi gato es feo.

g) Como mucha pizza .... me gusta el queso.

h) No voy a la piscina .... no puedo nadar.

Whoever said you can get by without conjunctions was telling porques...
I tried to write this without using any small linking words <u>but</u> it was impossible <u>because</u> they're everywhere.
That means they're super important <u>and</u> they'll improve your writing no end. Practise using them, <u>or</u> else.

How Often and How Much

Q1   Read the following statements about Sofía, then answer the questions in English.

> Voy al parque todos los días.
>
> Nunca juego al tenis.
>
> Siempre hago los deberes.
>
> A menudo voy al cine.
>
> Apenas voy de compras.
>
> Siempre desayuno cereales.

a) What does Sofía do every day? ....

b) How often does she play tennis? ....

c) What two things does she always do? ....

....

d) What does she often do? ....

e) How often does she go shopping? ....

Q2   Complete these sentences with the correct word from the box.

> a menudo   apenas   siempre   nunca

a) **I <u>never</u> drink milk for breakfast.** = ... bebo leche para el desayuno.

b) **You <u>always</u> go jogging.** = ... haces footing.

c) **I <u>often</u> watch TV.** = ... veo la televisión.

d) **She <u>rarely</u> goes to the theatre.** = ... va al teatro.

e) **I <u>always</u> have dinner at 7 o'clock.** = ... ceno a las siete.

f) **He <u>never</u> plays the flute.** = ... toca la flauta.

g) **They <u>often</u> go to the park.** = ... van al parque.

h) **We <u>rarely</u> play chess.** = ... jugamos al ajedrez.

> That's it,
> I'm calling it
> a knight...

Q3   Rewrite these sentences adding the correct word to give more detail. Use the words in the box to help you.

> muy   bastante   demasiado

a) David está cansado. .... [David is <u>very</u> tired.]

b) Susana es alta. .... [Susana is <u>quite</u> tall.]

c) Jaime come. .... [Jaime eats <u>too much</u>.]

d) Ana está contenta. .... [Ana is <u>very</u> happy.]

e) Gabriela habla. .... [Gabriela talks <u>too much</u>.]

f) Soy tímida. .... [I am <u>quite</u> shy.]

Giant Crossword

Q1   Use the clues to complete this crossword. All the answers should be **in Spanish**.

ACROSS
1) opposite of "malo" (5)
4) a place to buy medicine (8)
6) "I have"(5)
7) the trees = ... árboles (3)
8) short hair = pelo ...... (5)
11) the day when you celebrate becoming a year older (10)
14) the colour of the sky (4)
15) the house = ... casa (2)
17) "us" (8)
21) some books = ... libros (4)
23) opposite of east (5)
24) a + el = ... (2)
25) a female actor (6)
27) a feathered animal (6)

DOWN
1) a musical instrument you play by hitting it (7)
2) the month before June (4)
3) uno + uno = ... (3)
5) "builder" (7)
8) plural of "car" (6)
9) opposite of pretty (3)
10) the colour of snow (6)
12) "worse" (4)
13) "best wishes" — used when you sign off a letter (7)
16) your mother's mother is your .... (6)
18) hot drink, popular in the UK (2)
19) nueve + dos = ... (4)
20) a small red fruit (5)
22) a body part with a hand at the end of it (5)
26) it's your cat = es ...... gato (2)

Giant Crossword

Answers

Page 1

Q1 a) diez = 10
b) tres = 3
c) dos = 2
d) siete = 7
e) seis = 6
f) cinco = 5

Q2 b) siete – uno = seis
c) ocho + cuatro = doce
d) dieciocho + dos = veinte
e) catorce – trece = uno
f) quince – dos = trece

Q3 b) treinta y cuatro
c) treinta y nueve
d) ochenta y ocho
e) cuarenta y ocho
f) veintisiete
g) cuarenta y tres
h) cien
i) cincuenta y dos
j) setenta y ocho
k) setenta y tres
l) sesenta y uno
m) noventa y nueve
n) ochenta y seis
o) sesenta y cinco

Q4 b) segundo
c) quinto
d) cuarto
e) primero

Page 2

Q1

a) b)

c) d)

e) f)

Q2 b) Es la una menos veinte.
c) Son las seis y cuarto.
d) Son las siete menos diez.
e) Son las diez y veinticinco.
f) Son las once y veinte.

Q3 a) Friday
b) Sunday
c) Wednesday
d) Thursday
e) Tuesday
f) Saturday
g) on Fridays
h) Monday

Q4 a) mañana
b) el fin de semana
c) la tarde
d) ayer
e) la semana
f) la noche

Page 3

Q1 a) diciembre
b) agosto
c) octubre
d) febrero
e) abril

Q2 a) el veintidós de abril
b) el seis de octubre
c) el trece de enero
d) el catorce de julio
e) el seis de diciembre
f) el cinco de mayo

Q3 a) el diecisiete de septiembre
b) el veintidós de noviembre
c) el catorce de junio
d) el dos de marzo
e) el veintiuno de julio
f) el primero de enero

Page 4

Q1 a) Buenos días
b) Buenas tardes
c) Buenas noches

Q2 a) Hola
b) Adiós
c) Hasta luego
d) Hasta pronto

Q3 a) Buenas noches
b) Buenas tardes
c) Hola
d) ¿Qué tal?
e) Hasta luego
f) Buenos días

Q4 **Señor García**: Hola, Lucas.
Lucas: Buenos días, Señor García. ¿Cómo está?
Señor García: Bien, gracias. Hasta luego.
Lucas: Adiós, Señor García.

Page 5

Q1 a) Muy bien
b) Bien
c) Fatal
d) No muy bien

Q2
Encantado. → Pleased to meet you.
Le presento a mi tío. → Let me introduce my uncle.
¿Cómo está tu madre? → How is your mother?
Estoy muy bien, gracias. → I'm very well, thank you.
Este es mi hermano. → This is my brother.
Le presento a mi amigo. → Let me introduce my friend.
Esta es mi amiga, Olivia. → This is my friend, Olivia.

Q3 Arturo: Este es Ignacio. / Esta es Mireia.
Ignacio: Encantado.
Mireia: Encantada.

Page 6

Q1
a) gracias → thank you
b) por favor → please
c) lo siento → I'm sorry
d) de nada → you're welcome
e) muchas gracias → thank you very much

Q2 a) Perdone
b) Por favor
c) Con permiso

Q3 a) **Sofía**: Pilar, ¿quieres ir a la piscina mañana?
Pilar: Lo siento, pero no me gusta nadar.
Sofía: ¿Te gusta la playa?
Pilar: Lo siento mucho. Odio la playa también.

b) **Jaime**: Perdone, ¿hay un banco por aquí?
Alba: Sí. Está al lado del cine.
Jaime: Muchas gracias.
Alba: De nada.

c) **Teresa**: Buenos días.
Vendedora: ¿Sí señora?
Teresa: Tres kilos de plátanos, por favor.
Vendedora: ¿Algo más?
Teresa: No, gracias.

Page 7

Q1 a) Ana
b) Álvaro
c) Eva
d) Gabriel
e) David
f) María

Q2 b) ¿Puedo beber leche?
c) ¿Puedo ver la televisión?
d) ¿Puedo poner la mesa?
e) ¿Puedo escuchar música?
f) ¿Puedo jugar al fútbol?

Page 8

Q1 a) E.g. Tengo doce años.
b) E.g. Me llamo Oswald.
c) E.g. Mi cumpleaños es el dos de agosto.
d) E.g. Me gusta leer libros.

Q2 b) deportista
c) simpática
d) perezosa
e) tímido

Q3 b) Me llamo Jasmine. Soy baja. Tengo los ojos marrones y el pelo rubio.
c) Me llamo David. Tengo los ojos azules y el pelo negro. Llevo gafas.
d) Me llamo Sophie. Soy de talla mediana. Soy delgada y tengo el pelo largo.
e) Me llamo Gareth. Soy gordo. Soy pelirrojo. No llevo gafas.

Page 9

Q1 a) mi madre
b) mi abuelo
c) mi tío
d) mi hermana
e) mi padre
f) mi abuela
g) mi hermano
h) mi tía

Answers

Q2

Name	Age	Relationship
Jenny	35	mother
Peter	**40**	**stepfather**
Megan	16	stepsister
Joe	11	**brother**
Louise	**14**	best friend

Q3 a) Tengo dos hermanos y una hermana.
b) Me llamo Rebecca. Soy hija única.
c) Mi hermana se llama Emma y tiene diez años.
d) Mi primo se llama Matthew y es simpático.

Page 10

Q1 a) a dog
b) a horse
c) a bird

Q2

English	un/una	Spanish
cat	**un**	**gato**
mouse	**un**	**ratón**
tortoise	**una**	**tortuga**
hamster	**un**	**hámster**
rabbit	**un**	**conejo**

Q3 a) He has two black cats
b) Nerea
c) A horse
d) It's grey, it's called Ramito, it's very pretty
e) Emiliano

Q4 E.g. Tengo una tortuga y es muy perezosa.

Page 11

Q1 a) el cuarto de baño
b) la cocina
c) el comedor
d) el dormitorio
e) el jardín
f) el salón

Q2 a) una mesa
b) una cama
c) un armario
d) un sofá
e) una silla
f) un sillón

Q3 a) Six
b) Quite big
c) Three
d) A bed, a table and a wardrobe

Q4 a) E.g. Hay tres dormitorios, una cocina y un salón.
b) E.g. Hay una cama, un sillón y un armario.

Page 12

Q1 a) un piso / un apartamento
b) una casa
c) un pueblo
d) una ciudad

Q2 ¿Dónde vives?

Q3 Inés: Vivo en el noroeste de España.
Carlos: Vivo cerca del mar.
Patricia: Vivo en el este de España.
Sergio: Vivo en el sur de España.

Q4 Adriana: N
Ana: P/N
Orlando: P
María: P
Jorge: P
Antonia: P/N

Page 13

Q1 b) Hago <u>mis deberes</u>. — I do my homework.
c) Veo <u>la televisión</u>. — I watch TV.
d) Me lavo <u>los dientes</u>. — I brush my teeth.
e) Voy <u>al instituto</u>. — I go to school.

Q2 a) Ceno.
b) Me levanto.
c) Me visto.
d) Desayuno.
e) Me despierto.
f) Me acuesto.

Q3 b) Me lavo los dientes a las ocho menos cuarto.
c) Desayuno a las ocho y cuarto.
d) Hago mis deberes a las cuatro y veinte.
e) Veo la televisión a las seis.
f) Me acuesto a las nueve y media.

Page 14

Q1 a) <u>Lavo</u> los platos.
b) <u>Paso</u> la aspiradora.
c) <u>Arreglo</u> mi dormitorio.
d) <u>Hago</u> mi cama.
e) <u>Pongo</u> la mesa.

Q2 a) I do the shopping.
b) I wash the car.
c) I don't do anything.
d) I clean the house.

Q3 ¿Ayudas en casa?

Q4 b) Los lunes hago mi cama y arreglo mi dormitorio.
c) Los martes paso la aspiradora y hago la compra.
d) Pongo la mesa y lavo los platos.
e) No hago nada. Soy muy perezoso.

Page 15

Q1

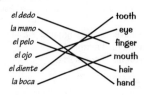

el dedo — finger
la mano — hand
el pelo — hair
el ojo — eye
el diente — tooth
la boca — mouth

Q2 b) la espalda — back
c) el brazo — arm
d) la rodilla — knee
e) el cuello — neck
f) la nariz — nose
g) la oreja — ear

Q3 a) la cabeza
b) el cuerpo

Q4 a) el pelo
b) el brazo
c) la mano
d) el estómago
e) la pierna
f) el pie

Page 16

Q1 a) unas pastillas
b) una tirita
c) una crema
d) un jarabe

Q2 a) <u>Me duele</u> la garganta.
b) <u>Me duelen</u> los ojos.
c) <u>Me duelen</u> los oídos.
d) <u>Me duele</u> el estómago.
e) <u>Me duele</u> la cabeza.
f) <u>Me duelen</u> los pies.

Q3 a) Iván and José
b) Sore throat
c) A syrup
d) José
e) His legs and his feet hurt
f) Lucía
g) Paula and Lucía

Page 17

Q1 a) las matemáticas
b) el inglés
c) la química
d) el español
e) la geografía
f) la informática
g) la música
h) el dibujo

Q2 a) la historia
b) la física
c) el alemán
d) la biología
e) la educación física
f) la religión
g) el francés
h) las ciencias

Q3 a) T
b) F
c) F
d) F
e) T

Q4 E.g Me gusta el español porque es interesante. No me gustan las ciencias porque son difíciles.

Page 18

Q1 b) Voy al instituto en bicicleta.
c) Voy al instituto en autobús.
d) Voy al instituto a pie.

Q2 a) By car
b) 8:45
c) 5
d) 1 hour
e) Lessons end
f) They have 2 hours every day.

Answers

Q3 a) <u>Me levanto</u> a las ocho.
  b) Las clases <u>comienzan</u> / <u>empiezan</u> a las nueve.
  c) Las clases <u>terminan</u> a las cuatro y media.
  d) <u>Tenemos</u> ocho clases por día.
  e) <u>Hacemos</u> una hora de deberes por día.

Page 19

Q1 a) un bolígrafo
  b) un lápiz
  c) una regla
  d) un alumno
  e) una goma

Q2 a) Stand up!
  b) Silence!
  c) Sit down!

Q3 a) False
  b) True
  c) What does that mean?
  d) How do you say it in English?
  e) How do you say it in Spanish?

Q4 b) <u>una</u> profesora   a teacher
  c) <u>un</u> cuaderno   an exercise book
  d) <u>un</u> horario   a timetable
  e) <u>una</u> clase   a lesson

Page 20

Q1 b) 7
  c) 1
  d) 5
  e) 3
  f) 6
  g) 2

Q2

enfermero	actriz	dentista
profesor	vendedora	albañil
peluquero	enfermera	policía

Q3 b) Pablo es actor.
  c) Carolina es médica.
  d) Blanca es peluquera.
  e) Carlos es dentista.
  f) Juan es mecánico.

Page 21

Q1a) The words should be in this order:
  restaurante
  semana
  hermano
  química
  hospital
  divertido

  b) i) F
  ii) F
  iii) T
  iv) F
  v) T
  vi) F

Q2 a) Quiero ser médico porque es útil.
  b) Quiero ser dentista porque es interesante.
  c) Quiero estudiar inglés porque es fácil.
  d) Quiero ser ingeniero porque ganan mucho dinero.
  e) Quiero estudiar dibujo porque es divertido.

Page 22

Q1

¿Dónde está el teatro? — How do I get to the market?
¿Para ir al mercado? — Where's the cinema?
¿Para ir a la iglesia? — Where's the theatre?
<u>¿Dónde está el cine?</u> — How do I get to the church?

Q2 a) <u>Siga</u> todo <u>recto</u>.
  b) Gire a la <u>derecha</u>.
  c) <u>Tome</u> la <u>segunda</u> calle a la izquierda.
  d) Tome la <u>primera</u> calle a la derecha.
  e) <u>Gire</u> a la izquierda.

Q3 b) the swimming pool
  c) the park
  d) the church
  e) the castle

Q4 a) T
  b) F
  c) F
  d) T

Page 23

Q1

English	el / la	Spanish
supermarket	**el**	**supermercado**
grocer's	**la**	tienda de comestibles
butcher's	**la**	**carnicería**
sweet shop	**la**	confitería
newsagent's	**el**	**quiosco**
baker's	**la**	panadería

Q2

la farmacia — bank
el banco — cake shop
el mercado — pharmacy
la biblioteca — library
la pastelería — market

Q3 a) la tienda de comestibles
  b) el banco
  c) la farmacia
  d) la carnicería
  e) la librería
  f) la pastelería

Page 24

Q1 b) un parque
  c) una iglesia
  d) un museo
  e) un ayuntamiento
  f) un castillo

Q2 a) Bárbara
  b) Bárbara and Pablo

  c) Pablo
  d) Pablo
  e) Ángela
  f) Ángela

Q3 a) En mi ciudad/pueblo, hay un castillo.
  b) No hay piscina.
  c) Hay un museo y un parque.
  d) Hay un ayuntamiento y una iglesia.
  e) No hay estación en mi ciudad/pueblo.

Page 25

Q1

la fresa
la manzana
el limón
la naranja
el plátano
la pera
el melocotón

Q2 a) la patata
  b) la zanahoria
  c) la coliflor
  d) el tomate
  e) los guisantes
  f) las judías
  g) el champiñón
  h) la cebolla

Q3 b) la carne de cerdo
  c) el pollo
  d) los mariscos
  e) el cordero
  f) el jamón
  g) el pescado
  h) la salchicha

Page 26

Q1

el chocolate
la galleta
el pastel
la mermelada
el azúcar
el helado

Q2 b) el yogur = yogurt
  c) la leche = milk
  d) la nata = cream
  e) el huevo = egg
  f) el queso = cheese

Q3 b) coffee
  c) tea
  d) hot chocolate
  e) lemonade
  f) orange juice
  g) mineral water
  h) red wine
  i) white wine
  j) beer

Q4 a) los cereales
  b) las patatas fritas
  c) el arroz
  d) la sopa
  e) el bocadillo
  f) el pan
  g) la pasta
  h) la hamburguesa

Answers

Page 27

Q1   Esteban likes:
ice cream, chocolate, strawberries, pears, bananas
Esteban doesn't like:
lettuce, cauliflower, peas, steak

Q2   Ben: No, no tengo sed.
Abi: Meg, ¿tienes hambre?
Meg: Sí, tengo hambre.

Q3 b)   Como cereales y bebo café.
c)   Almuerzo a las doce y media.
d)   Como un bocadillo de jamón.
e)   Ceno a las siete y cuarto.
f)   Como pollo, arroz y zanahorias.

Page 28

Q1 a)   la camarera
b)   la carta
c)   el primer plato
d)   la cuenta
e)   el postre
f)   el restaurante
g)   el plato principal

Q2 a)   Una mesa para uno, por favor.
b)   Quisiera la ensalada, por favor.
c)   Quisiera el pescado con arroz.
d)   Quisiera el pastel de chocolate.
e)   Quisiera un agua mineral.
f)   La cuenta, por favor.

Page 29

Q1 a)   los pantalones
b)   el jersey
c)   la camisa
d)   los calcetines
e)   la falda
f)   el sombrero
g)   el vestido
h)   la chaqueta
i)   la camiseta
j)   los zapatos

Q2 a)   Antonio
b)   David
c)   A skirt and T-shirt
d)   A dress

Q3   Nadia: Llevo una falda <u>verde</u>, un <u>jersey</u> naranja, un sombrero <u>azul</u>, unos zapatos <u>rojos</u> y unos calcetines <u>amarillos</u>.
José: Llevo unos <u>pantalones</u> rojos, una camisa <u>rosa</u>, una corbata <u>blanca</u>, una <u>chaqueta</u> marrón, unos <u>calcetines</u> negros y unos zapatos <u>grises</u>.

Q4   E.g. Llevo una camisa blanca, una chaqueta negra, una falda negra, una corbata negra, amarilla y azul y unos zapatos negros.

Page 30

Q1

¿Algo más? — I would like a skirt.
¿Tiene calcetines? — Is that all?
¿En qué puedo servirle? — How much is it?
¿Es todo? — Do you have any socks?
¿Cuánto cuesta? — Anything else?
Quisiera una falda. — How can I help you?

Q2 b)   Cuestan veinticinco euros.
c)   Cuesta dieciocho euros.
d)   Cuesta veintitrés euros.
e)   ¿Cuánto cuestan unos pantalones?
f)   ¿Cuánto cuesta un sombrero?
g)   ¿Cuánto cuestan unos calcetines?

Q3 a)   Quisiera un sombrero azul (por favor).
b)   ¿Cuánto cuesta?
c)   Lo compro.

Page 31

Q1 a)   el fútbol
b)   el tenis
c)   el baloncesto
d)   el hockey
e)   el ajedrez
f)   el ping-pong

Q2 a)   3
b)   2
c)   the cello
d)   the flute and the clarinet
e)   the trumpet and the guitar

Q3 a)   Juego
b)   Toco
c)   Toco
d)   Juego
e)   Juego

Q4 a)   Toco el violoncelo.
b)   Juego al baloncesto.
c)   Juego al rugby.
d)   Toco la batería.

Page 32

Q1 a)   voy a nadar
b)   hago senderismo
c)   hago footing
d)   hago aerobic
e)   voy de compras
f)   hago ciclismo

Q2 a)   Hiking.
b)   It's fun.
c)   It's tiring.
d)   It's easy.
e)   Jogging.

Q3 a)   Me gusta hacer <u>ciclismo</u> porque es <u>fácil</u>.
b)   No me gusta hacer <u>senderismo</u> porque es <u>aburrido</u>.
c)   Me encanta hacer <u>aerobic</u> porque es <u>divertido</u>.
d)   Odio hacer <u>footing</u> porque es <u>difícil</u>.

Page 33

Q1

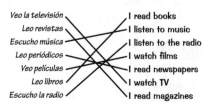

Veo la televisión — I watch TV
Leo revistas — I read magazines
Escucho música — I listen to music
Leo periódicos — I read newspapers
Veo películas — I watch films
Leo libros — I read books
Escucho la radio — I listen to the radio

Q2 a)   Venus
b)   Lisa
c)   Magazines
d)   Vincent
e)   Venus and Vincent
f)   Newspapers
g)   Lisa

Q3 a)   Me gusta esta película.
b)   No me gusta esta película.
c)   Me gusta este libro.
d)   No me gusta este libro.

Page 34

Q1 b)   la piscina
c)   el teatro
d)   el parque
e)   el cine
f)   el polideportivo
g)   mi casa

Q2 b)   Vamos al teatro.
c)   Vamos al parque.
d)   Vamos al cine.
e)   Vamos a la piscina.
f)   Vamos al restaurante.

Q3 a)   F
b)   T
c)   F
d)   F
e)   T
f)   T
g)   F

Page 35

Q1

Person	Meeting Place	Time
Rubén	in the town centre	10.45
Carmen	**in front of the swimming pool**	**10.15**
Iker	**at Iker's house**	**3.00**
Yolanda	**at the theatre**	**8.30**
Patricio	**in front of the cinema**	**9.00**

Q2
Renato: Hello Marta. Let's go to the town centre.
Marta: Great. Where shall we meet and when shall we meet?
Renato: Let's meet in front of the theatre at 12 o'clock

Q3 a)   ¿Cuánto cuesta una entrada?
b)   Cuesta seis euros.
c)   Quisiera dos entradas por favor.

Page 36

Q1 a)   bus
b)   el autocar
c)   plane
d)   el barco
e)   el coche
f)   the underground
g)   la motocicleta
h)   bike

Answers

Q2 a) By train.
 b) On foot.
 c) Clara.
 d) By underground.
 e) The park.

Q3 a) Voy al instituto en autobús.
 b) Voy al teatro en tren.
 c) Voy al quiosco a pie.
 d) Voy al supermercado en coche.
 e) Voy al polideportivo en bicicleta.
 f) Voy de vacaciones en avión.
 g) Voy a Francia en barco.

Page 37
Q1 a) ¿Cuándo sale el tren para Málaga?
 b) ¿De qué andén sale el tren?
 c) El tren sale del andén número seis.
 d) ¿Cuándo llega el tren a Málaga?

Q2 b) Quisiera un billete de ida / sencillo, de primera clase, para Segovia.
 c) Quisiera un billete de ida y vuelta, de primera clase, para Ávila.
 d) Quisiera un billete de ida y vuelta, de segunda clase, para Cuenca.

Q3 a) 10.30
 b) 5
 c) Córdoba
 d) 5.15
 e) Málaga
 f) 1

Page 38
Q1

Q2 a) A stamp
 b) 1.50 euros
 c) an envelope
 d) Where is the post box?

Q3 a) Mi número de teléfono es el veintitrés, cincuenta y cuatro, noventa y uno.
 b) Hola. Soy Vicente.
 c) ¿Puedo hablar con Philip, por favor?

Page 39
Q1 a) Gracias por tu carta.
 b) Querido John.
 c) Un abrazo.
 d) ¿Qué tal?
 e) Escríbeme pronto.

Q2 a) Bilbao, 20 de agosto
 b) Querido Santi,
 c) Me alegró mucho oír de ti.
 d) Hasta pronto
 e) Yolanda

Q3 Answers should include this information:
  Your hometown, a date
 Querida Ana,
  ¿Qúe tal? Gracias por tu carta.
  Escríbeme pronto.
 Saludos,
  Your name.

Page 40
Q1 a) 1
 b) 4
 c) 3
 d) 5

Q2 a) F
 b) F
 c) F
 d) T
 e) T
 f) F

Q3 Answers should include this information:
  Your hometown, a date
 Estimada señora Domínguez,
  Quisiera quedarme desde el 5 de agosto hasta el 9 de agosto.
  Quisiera dos habitaciones dobles.
  ¿Cuánto cuesta?
 Le saluda atentamente,
  Your name and surname

Page 41
Q1 a) It's nice weather
 b) It's foggy
 c) It's windy
 d) It's cold
 e) It's bad weather
 f) It's very hot

Q2 a) Hace sol
 b) Está lloviendo
 c) Hace calor
 d) Está nevando
 e) Hay tormenta
 f) Está nublado

Q3 a) En Barcelona está lloviendo.
 b) En Málaga hace sol.
 c) En Bilbao está nevando.
 d) En Madrid está nublado.
 e) En Sevilla hace viento.
 f) En Valencia hay tormenta.

Q4 a) Julio es un mes en el verano.
 b) Diciembre es un mes en el invierno.
 c) Octubre es un mes en el otoño.
 d) Abril es un mes en la primavera.

Page 42
Q1 b) 5
 c) 1
 d) 6
 e) 7
 f) 3
 g) 2

Q2 a) To the south of Portugal
 b) With her mother, step-father and brother
 c) By car
 d) For two weeks
 e) In a hotel
 f) It's very hot

Q3 a) Normalmente voy a Italia.
 b) Voy con mis amigos / mis amigas.
 c) Paso diez días allí.
 d) Hace calor y sol.

Page 43
Q1 a) la caravana
 b) el saco de dormir
 c) el agua potable
 d) la tienda
 e) la parcela

Q2 b) una habitación doble con balcón
 c) una habitación individual con baño
 d) una habitación doble con ducha
 e) una habitación doble con baño

Q3 a) el hotel
 b) la llave
 c) la habitación
 d) el teléfono
 e) el albergue juvenil
 f) el camping
 g) el comedor
 h) los servicios

Page 44
Q1 a) E
 b) P
 c) P
 d) E

Q2 The words should be in this order:
 individual
 baño
 cuántas
 tres
 euros
 llave

Q3 a) ¿Tiene una parcela libre?
 b) Quisiera una parcela para una caravana.
 c) Quisiera quedarme cinco noches.

Page 45
Q1
Gran Bretaña — Great Britain
Inglaterra — England
Escocia — Scotland
País de Gales — Wales
Irlanda del Norte — Northern Ireland
Reino Unido — United Kingdom

Q2 b) Germany
 c) Ireland
 d) Switzerland
 e) Belgium
 f) France

Q3 b) Vivo en Portugal.
 c) Vivo en España.
 d) Vivo en Austria.

Q4 a) Francia
 b) España
 c) Italia

Answers

Page 46

Q1 b) French ♂
   c) Spanish ♂
   d) Northern Irish ♂
   e) Welsh ♂
   f) Scottish ♀
   g) Italian ♀
   h) German ♀

Q2 b) Soy irlandés.
   c) Soy francesa.
   d) Soy español.
   e) Soy italiana.
   f) Soy galés.

Q3 a) F
   b) T
   c) T
   d) F
   e) T
   f) F

Page 47

Q1 b) Me gusta el dibujo.
   c) Odio la geografía.
   d) No me gusta la informática.
   e) Me encantan las ciencias.
   f) Me gustan las matemáticas.

Q2 a) interesante
   b) fácil
   c) divertido
   d) aburrido
   e) raro
   f) difícil
   g) estupendo
   h) bueno
   i) horrible
   j) precioso

Q3 b) Me gusta escuchar la radio porque es interesante.
   c) Odio lavar el coche porque es horrible.
   d) Me encantan los deportes porque son divertidos.

Page 48

Q1
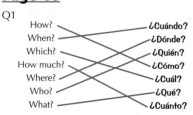

How? — ¿Cuándo?
When? — ¿Dónde?
Which? — ¿Quién?
How much? — ¿Cómo?
Where? — ¿Cuál?
Who? — ¿Qué?
What? — ¿Cuánto?

  a) ¿Qué hay en tu dormitorio?
  b) ¿Cuándo te levantas?
  c) ¿Cuál es tu color preferido?
  e) ¿Quién quiere tarta?
  f) ¿Cuánto cuesta?
  g) ¿Dónde está Kelis?

Q2 a) When is your birthday?
   b) How much does a lemonade cost?
   c) Where does Sandra live?
   d) What time do you eat?
   e) How is your mother?
   f) Who is Alexis?

Page 49 (middle column)

Q3 b) ¿Cómo te llamas?
   c) ¿Cuánto cuesta el libro?
   d) ¿Cuándo sale el tren?
   e) ¿Cómo vas al instituto?
   f) ¿Qué hay en tu dormitorio?

Page 49

Q1 a) M
   b) F
   c) F
   d) M
   e) M
   f) F
   g) M
   h) F
   i) F

Q2 a) dos perros
   b) dos peras
   c) dos granjas
   d) dos armarios
   e) dos primos
   f) dos calles
   g) dos bicicletas
   h dos tomates
   i) dos revistas
   j) dos vestidos
   k) dos parques
   l) dos clases

Q3 a) dos trenes
   b) dos actrices
   c) dos ratones
   d) dos yogures
   e) dos árboles
   f) dos melones
   g) dos lápices
   h) dos narices

Q4 a) hermanas
   b) plátanos
   c) coches
   d) albañiles
   e) habitaciones
   f) pasteles
   g) sillones

Page 50

Q1 b) las revistas
   c) el médico
   d) las corbatas
   e) el bocadillo
   f) la tirita
   g) los actores
   h) el restaurante
   i) las reglas
   j) la trompeta

Q2 a) El banco está enfrente del supermercado.
   b) El cine está al lado de la farmacia.
   c) Para ir al banco, tome la primera calle a la derecha.
   d) La estación está al final de la calle.
   e) Para ir a la playa, tome la segunda calle a la izquierda.

Q3 unas patatas
   unos huevos
   unos plátanos
   una cebolla
   un melocotón

Page 51 (top right)

Q4 b) No tengo hermanos.
   c) No tengo bolígrafo.
   d) No tengo dinero.

Page 51

Q1
she — ella
you (singular) — tú
I — yo
we — nosotros
they (feminine) — ellas
you (plural) — vosotros
he — él
they (masculine) — ellos

Q2 b) Él tiene ocho años.
   c) Ellas están en la playa.
   d) Ellos juegan al fútbol.
   e) Nosotros vamos de compras.
   f) Vosotros sois tímidos.

Q3 a) Mi abuela nos visita.
   b) Janice y Deborah me ven.
   c) Te conozco.
   d) Os miro.

Q4 a) Mi madre la limpia.
   b) Ellos los lavan.
   c) Rafael las compra.
   d) Natalia los quiere.
   e) Nosotros lo bebemos.

Page 52

Q1

masculine singular	feminine singular	masculine plural	feminine plural
pequeño	**pequeña**	pequeños	pequeñas
alto	alta	**altos**	altas
viejo	**vieja**	viejos	**viejas**
blanco	blanca	**blancos**	**blancas**
bonito	**bonita**	**bonitos**	bonitas

Q2 a) Mi casa no es muy grande.
   b) Las sillas son raras.
   c) Mi amiga es inteligente.
   d) Mi hermana es trabajadora.
   e) Estos deberes son difíciles.
   f) Mis pantalones son verdes y largos.
   g) Mi primo es horrible pero mi tía es simpática.
   h) Tengo dos lápices rojos y un bolígrafo negro.

Q3 Luisa   Llevo un vestido blanco.
   Augustín   Me gustan mis tortugas verdes.
   Rodolfo   Quiero una pizza grande.
   Ornella   Tengo unos libros buenos.

Page 53

Q1 a) El alemán es menos difícil.
   b) Esos gatos son los más gordos.
   c) Esta clase es la más fácil.
   d) Mi libro es menos interesante.
   e) Las gafas de Tim son las más grandes.

Answers

Q2 a) Marcos es <u>joven</u> pero Pablito es <u>menor</u>. Su hermana Romina es <u>la menor</u>.

b) La historia es <u>mala</u> pero el inglés es <u>peor</u>. El dibujo es <u>el peor</u>.

c) Mi ratón es <u>viejo</u> pero mi gato es <u>mayor</u>. Mi perro es <u>el mayor</u>.

d) Tu postre es <u>bueno</u> pero su postre es <u>mejor</u>. Mi postre es <u>el mejor</u>.

Q3 b) Grizelda es <u>menos alta que</u> (*or* <u>más baja que</u>) Bob.

c) Bob es <u>tan alto como</u> Neil.

d) Neil es <u>más alto que</u> Carlos.

Page 54

Q1 a) <u>Mi</u> hermana es enfermera.

b) <u>Tus</u> orejas son muy grandes.

c) ¿Dónde están <u>sus</u> padres?

d) <u>Mis</u> zapatos son muy cómodos.

e) ¿<u>Sus</u> deberes son difíciles?

f) <u>Tus</u> libros están en <u>su</u> cama.

g) <u>Mi</u> tío es <u>tu</u> profesor.

Q2 a) <u>Nuestra</u> abuela es inteligente.

b) <u>Vuestras</u> casas están cerca.

c) <u>Nuestros</u> perros son simpáticos.

d) <u>Vuestros</u> primos viven con <u>nuestras</u> primas.

e) <u>Nuestra</u> madre y <u>vuestro</u> padre son actores.

Q3

the book	el libro
this book	**este libro**
that book	ese libro
these books	**estos libros**
those books	**esos libros**

the shirt	la camisa
this shirt	esta camisa
that shirt	**esa camisa**
these shirts	**estas camisas**
those shirts	**esas camisas**

Q4 a) <u>Ese</u> plátano es <u>tu</u> plátano.

b) <u>Estas</u> peras son <u>mis</u> peras.

c) <u>Esos</u> chicos son <u>sus</u> hermanos.

Page 55

Q1 You should have ticked:

a) Voy a la piscina para nadar.

b) El coche pasa por el túnel.

c) El libro es para ti.

d) Pago siete euros por la entrada.

e) El tren para Girona sale a la una.

f) Voy al centro por la mañana.

Q2 a) para

b) por

c) para

d) por

e) por

f) para

g) por

h) para

i) por

j) para

Q3 a) ¿Hay un tren <u>para</u> Valencia?

b) Pagó dos euros <u>por</u> el bolígrafo.

c) Voy al parque <u>para</u> jugar al fútbol.

d) Lavé el coche <u>por</u> la tarde.

e) El pescado es <u>para</u> ti.

f) Gracias <u>por</u> el libro.

g) Las chicas fueron <u>por</u> la panadería.

Page 56

Q1
tú <u>bebes</u>
él / ella <u>bebe</u>
ellos / ellas <u>beben</u>
vosotros <u>bebéis</u>
yo <u>bebo</u>
nosotros <u>bebemos</u>

Q2 a) bailamos

b) dibuja

c) escucho

d) cantan

e) trabajáis

f) nadas

Q3 a) recibo

b) partes

c) sube

d) abrimos

e) escribís

f) deciden

Q4 a) cantamos

b) asisto

c) corre

d) aprende

e) decidís

f) ayudas

Page 57

Q1 a) quiere

b) quieren

c) quiero

d) quieres

e) queremos

f) queréis

Q2 a) tengo

b) tienen

c) tienes

d) tenéis

e) tiene

f) tenemos

Q3 b) Podemos beber agua.

c) Puede jugar al fútbol.

d) Pueden tocar la flauta.

e) Puedes nadar.

f) Podéis leer.

g) Puedo hablar francés.

Q4 a) 2

b) 14 and 16 years old

c) A cat (called Bopi)

d) Because she can speak English

Page 58

Q1 b) ir

c) estar

d) ser

e) ir

f) ser

g) ser

h) estar

Q2 a) estoy

b) es

c) van

d) está

e) eres

f) voy

g) son

h) estamos

Q3 The words should be in this order:
estás
estoy
Soy
es
vamos
van
son

Q4 a) En mi estuche <u>hay</u> un lápiz que <u>es</u> gris.

b) Mi dormitorio <u>es</u> grande pero la cocina <u>es</u> pequeña.

c) En mi dormitorio <u>hay</u> una cama, una mesa y una silla, pero no <u>hay</u> televisión.

d) La historia <u>es</u> muy aburrida pero el inglés <u>es</u> muy interesante.

e) <u>Hay</u> muchos museos en Londres porque <u>es</u> la capital de Inglaterra.

Page 59

Q1

	SER	ESTAR
	a	**c**
	b	d
	e	f
	g	
	h	

Q2 You should have ticked:

a) Su pelo es negro.

b) Mi hermano está muy contento hoy.

c) Madrid está en el centro de España.

d) Mi padre es médico.

e) Estamos en el parque.

f) Estoy muy triste.

Q3 a) Mi tío <u>es</u> mecánico.

b) <u>Es</u> trabajador.

c) <u>Estoy</u> enfermo.

d) <u>Están</u> en el restaurante.

e) Sus ojos <u>son</u> azules.

f) Grizebeck <u>está</u> en Inglaterra.

g) <u>Eres</u> deportista.

h) Esta <u>es</u> mi madre.

Page 60

Q1 b) Me levanto

c) Me ducho

d) Me visto

e) Me acuesto

f) Me lavo los dientes

Q2 a) se

b) nos

c) te

d) se

e) os

f) me

Answers

Q3 b) David se levanta a las siete y cuarto.
c) David se ducha a las siete y media.
d) David se acuesta a las diez y cuarto.

Q4 b) Se lava los dientes.
c) Te duchas.
d) Os laváis.
e) Nos acostamos.
f) Se visten.

Page 61

Q1 a) F
b) T
c) T
d) T
e) F
f) F

Q2 b) No me lavo los dientes.
c) No tenemos dinero.
d) No quiero ver la película.
e) No van al cine.
f) Mi hermano no es alto.
g) Harry no quiere leer.

Q3 a) No voy <u>nunca</u> a la piscina.
b) No hablamos <u>nunca</u> en clase.
c) No como <u>nada</u> para el desayuno.
d) No me escuchas <u>nunca</u>.
e) No hace <u>nada</u> los fines de semana.
f) No veo <u>nada</u>.

Page 62

Q1

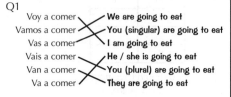

Voy a comer — We are going to eat
Vamos a comer — You (singular) are going to eat
Vas a comer — I am going to eat
Vais a comer — He / she is going to eat
Van a comer — You (plural) are going to eat
Va a comer — They are going to eat

Q2 b) El martes <u>va a jugar</u> al tenis.
c) El miércoles <u>va a nadar</u>.
d) El jueves <u>va a hacer</u> ciclismo.
e) El viernes <u>va a ir</u> de compras.
f) El sábado <u>va a hacer</u> senderismo.
g) El domingo <u>va a ver</u> la televisión.

Q3 a) <u>Vais a</u> hacer los deberes.
b) <u>Vamos a</u> hacer esquí.
c) <u>Van a</u> jugar al baloncesto.
d) <u>Vas a</u> lavar el coche.
e) <u>Voy a</u> escuchar la radio.
f) <u>No va a</u> hacer footing.
g) <u>No voy a</u> comer las galletas.

Page 63

Q1 a) Speak!
b) Walk!
c) Start!
d) Do your homework!
e) Be kind!
f) Come!

Q2 b) ¡come!
c) ¡salta!
d) ¡abre!
e) ¡escucha!
f) ¡corre!
g) ¡ve!
h) ¡ten!

Q3 a) 1
b) 6
c) 4
d) 5
e) 2
f) 3

Q4 b) ¡<u>Mire</u> la pizarra!
c) ¡<u>Escuche</u> la música!
d) ¡<u>Abra</u> la ventana!
e) ¡<u>Escriba</u> una carta!

Page 64

Q1 b) nadó
c) bailaste
d) esquiamos
e) escuchasteis
f) cantaron

Q2 a) comí
b) volvió
c) perdimos
d) entendiste
e) aprendisteis
f) corrieron

Q3 a) sufrí
b) escribimos
c) subieron
d) abriste
e) decidió
f) vivisteis

Q4

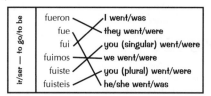

ir/ser — to go/to be
fueron — I went/was
fue — they went/were
fui — you (singular) went/were
fuimos — we went/were
fuiste — you (plural) went/were
fuisteis — he/she went/was

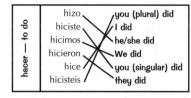

hacer — to do
hizo — you (plural) did
hiciste — I did
hicimos — he/she did
hicieron — We did
hice — you (singular) did
hicisteis — they did

Page 65

Q1 a) a
b) de
c) de
d) de
e) a
f) a
g) de
h) a

Q2 a) Vamos <u>al</u> restaurante.
b) Voy <u>al</u> banco.
c) Los actores son <u>del</u> teatro.
d) Quiero ir <u>a la</u> piscina.
e) ¿El bolígrafo es <u>del</u> profesor?
f) La carta es <u>de la</u> secretaria.

Q3 El hombre está <u>en</u> la tienda.
El fuego está <u>delante de</u> la tienda.
La vaca está <u>detrás de</u> la tienda.
El ratón está <u>debajo de</u> la vaca.
El perro está <u>al lado de</u> la tienda.

Page 66

Q1 b) Hablamos francés e inglés.
c) Diego compra patatas y leche.
d) Sara es simpática e inteligente.
e) Pedro hace ciclismo y senderismo.
f) Hugo tiene un gato y un pez.

Q2

¿Prefieres rojo — o té?
¿Juegas al fútbol — o verde?
¿Vas en tren — o al parque?
¿Quieres café — o al tenis?
¿Quieres escuchar música — o en autobús?
¿Vas al polideportivo — o ver la televisión?

Q3 a) porque
b) pero
c) pero
d) porque
e) pero
f) pero
g) porque
h) porque

Page 67

Q1 a) goes to the park
b) never
c) her homework and has cereal for breakfast
d) goes to the cinema
e) rarely

Q2 a) Nunca
b) Siempre
c) A menudo
d) Apenas
e) Siempre
f) Nunca
g) A menudo
h) Apenas

Q3 a) David está <u>muy</u> cansado.
b) Susana es <u>bastante</u> alta.
c) Jaime come <u>demasiado</u>.
d) Ana está <u>muy</u> contenta.
e) Gabriela habla <u>demasiado</u>.
f) Soy <u>bastante</u> tímida.

Page 68